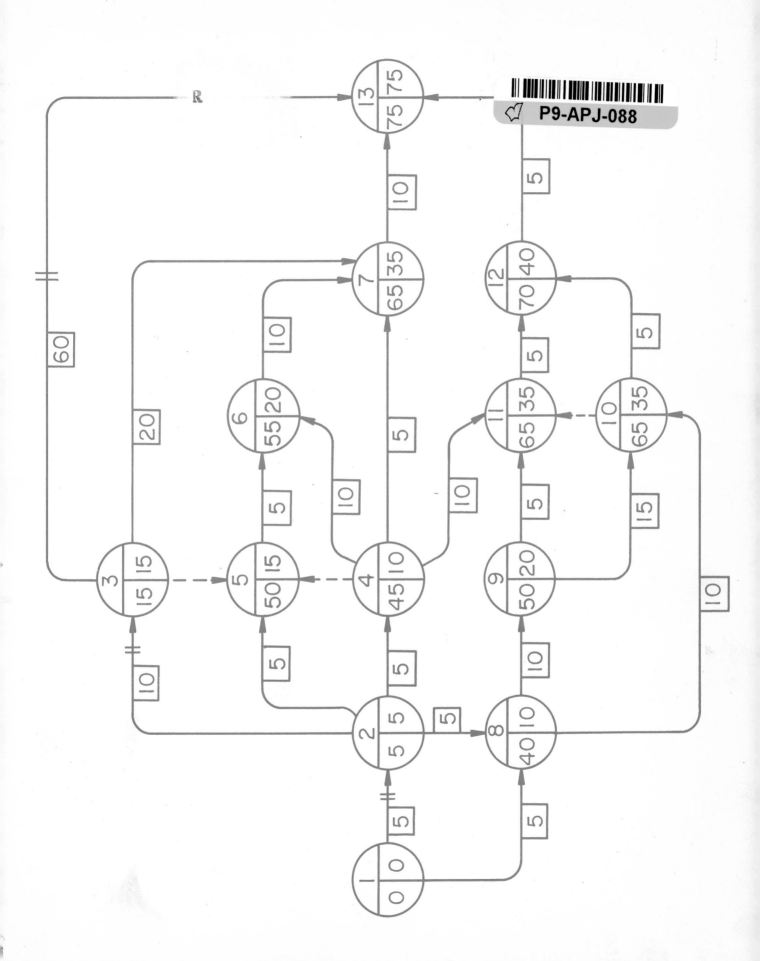

P9-APJ-088

Project Management and Control

VOLUME I

Finding the Critical Path

R. L. MARTINO, Ph.D.

Project Management and Control

VOLUME I

Finding the Critical Path

American Management Association

New York

Copyright © 1964 by the American Management Association, Inc. Printed in the United States of America by The Comet Press, Inc.

All rights reserved. This book may not be reproduced in whole or in part without the express permission of the Association.

Library of Congress catalog card number: 64-18544

First Printing

HD
69
P7
M3
V.1
c.2

G010 Ag71

4B

Preface to *Project Management and Control*

Dᴜʀɪɴɢ ᴛʜᴇ ᴘᴀsᴛ sɪx ʏᴇᴀʀs I have discussed and used PERT and CPM with many people in many places. Whether with a company president or a foreman on a construction site, whether for a billion-dollar project or one costing a few hundred, whether in the United States, Canada, or Europe—two things have become clear. First, PERT and CPM are becoming indispensably necessary. Second, there is some confusion over their nature and use.

In the early days of PERT and CPM people told me that the techniques were not necessary because they embodied nothing new. "Who's using them?" they asked. Today, PERT and CPM are fashionable, and many experts and "fathers" exist. Furthermore, there are almost 50 variations, all with different acronyms. There are much opportunism, me-tooism, and bandwagonry. This faddism can obscure the truth, but, more important, it can lead to disenchantment when "PERT and CPM fail."

A long time ago, a very clever man said, "There is no royal road to learning." PERT and CPM are techniques; they are only as effective as the ability and experience of the user permit them to be. The rules are simple; their application, however, is *not* simple because it requires an analysis of what is to be done. We all tend to prefer to be "doing and planning by ear," rather than to plan before doing. Giving in to this tendency results in chaos. I think we are all familiar with the signs which indicate that planning is required.

5

PLAN AHEAD

There are currently literally thousands of applications of PERT and CPM. They vary from something as gigantic as our space program to something as common as replacing a valve in a steel plant. The projects vary in cost from a few hundred dollars to several billion. PERT and CPM are universal in the sense of their range of applications, both by type of project and by size.

I hope in this book to present to the reader, in non-technical language, the essence of PERT and CPM. I have a strong dislike of any book which presupposes that I know everything about its subject before I start reading it. I trust I have carried this bias as a reader into my efforts as a writer. I have found it necessary to be redundant in order to be clear. To those more quick-witted than I, my apologies for this redundancy.

When giving courses on the subject in conference room, classroom, and briefing room, it is easier to make a point by drawing a simple diagram and singling out the particular parts of the diagram referred to. This diagrammatic approach, with a heavy reliance on reference to specific parts of a diagram, has been incorporated into this book. My objective, as stated, is to explain what PERT and CPM are and how to use them profitably to solve problems. But it has seemed impossible to do this in just one volume. Consequently, the editors and I have decided to issue the material in two separate volumes. The first is entitled *Finding the Critical Path* and is devoted to the basics of both PERT and CPM; the second volume, entitled *Applied Operational Planning*, deals with the use of these basics in project management and control, covering the subjects of PERT/COST and resource allocation and scheduling.

Many people may require only the first volume in preparing an arrow diagram and in finding the critical path. Others with perhaps more knowledge of the basics will be mainly interested in the second. Both volumes, however, are required for an understanding of the PERT/CPM concept as a whole. In particular, I call the attention of the reader to Chapter Seven of *Finding the Critical Path*, which does, I believe, invalidate much of the literature published to date on the way to use PERT in project planning.

There is no doubt that PERT and CPM are revolutionizing the concept and method of project management and control. PERT and CPM are fashionable today (1964) because of the hard work and earnestness of the pioneers. Certain individuals stand out for their tremendous contributions to the state of the art. Some were developers or creators of the techniques, some spearheaded the initial applications to justify the worth of the techniques, and some, in positions of authority, were convinced that these unknown techniques could help them. Their number is endless, and to attempt to select "the" list for the entire field of PERT and CPM would undoubtedly lead to omissions. There are, however, certain individuals with whom I have worked, or for whom I did work, who stand out for contributions which led to this particular book. These people are Dr. John W. Mauchly; James E. Kelley, Jr.; Morgan R. Walker; Ian D. Ritson; Air Vice Marshal C. F. Johns; Colonel E. Churchill; E. S. Steben; John R. Hopkins; and Borge Christensen.

Jim Kelley and Morgan Walker developed the original mathematics and the approach of what is now termed CPM. John Mauchly was the coordinating influence who brought Kelley, Walker, himself, and me together as Mauchly Associates in 1959. Ian Ritson, now with Olin Mathieson Chemical Corporation, believed in the capabilities of CPM in 1959 and, while with Perini Ltd., convinced top management to try it. He carried this conviction to Olin Mathieson, which is now one of the more advanced users of PERT and CPM in its project work.

Air Vice Marshal Johns (Assistant Deputy Minister of National Defence in Canada) and Colonel Churchill (Director of Special Projects for the Canadian Army) believed that these techniques could help them in certain aspects of their work. This led to extensive work with the Canadian Government during the spring and summer of 1960. Stan Steben, then Major Steben, was a dedicated and dynamic worker and "critical path enthusiast" all through that period (and has remained so since).

Some of the more "practical" aspects outlined in these volumes were developed, because of need, during this period. In particular, the concepts of resource allocation and scheduling were formulated and first applied in a rudimentary fashion at that time. I have since incorporated additional developments in these techniques and have called the overall approach MAP.*

Throughout the period, Jack Hopkins, now with UNIVAC, worked with me. I am indebted to him for much constructive criticism and suggestion.

I first met Borge Christensen, of General Electric, in September 1960 when he registered in a course I was conducting on CPM and MAP in Toronto. To him I am indebted for the manner in which he grasped the potential scope of PERT and CPM applications. His efforts led to the development of the CPM package for the G.E. 225. I shall always remember with nostalgia the time spent in Phoenix in May 1961 working with Borge to train G.E. Computer Department personnel and prepare the "225 Package."

Acknowledgment must also be made of the fine contributions of Admiral W. F. Rayborn and of the Special Projects Office of the U.S. Navy in spearheading the development and application of PERT on the Polaris program. The team of men from Booz, Allen and Hamilton, headed by Don Malcolm, deserve credit for developing PERT/Time.

---

*I first called it Manpower Allocation Procedure to avoid the acronym RAP for Resource Allocation Procedure. Now I call it Multiple Allocation Procedure. In any event, I like the acronym MAP, and we can always say it's "Martino's Allocation Procedure."

It goes without saying that I am indebted to the Olin Mathieson Chemical Corporation. When I was a "Mauchly Associate," that company was very receptive to the use of operational planning. Now, as a member of the corporate staff, I am even more pleased, looking on the inside, at the caliber of the work and the ability of the people doing it.

PERT and CPM are based on the premise that planning and scheduling are two separate and distinct functions. There is nothing new in any of the basic elements of these techniques. However, the manner in which all of the known concepts are rearranged is new—even revolutionary. This thought may be appreciated by considering radio and television. The components of the television set are not new. All of them were known when there was no television. Many of them were used in radio and often in exactly the same fashion as they are used in television. What is remarkably new in television is that by rearranging the known (or old) components, we suddenly get sight as well as sound—picture as well as voice.

PERT and CPM are, in that sense, the video of project management and control. By rearranging the basic and known elements, we proceed from "voice" alone to the clarity of a project plan and schedule.

No book can ever replace actual experience. This work is meant to provide the basic and fundamental information concerning the use of PERT and CPM. Applying the principles outlined in these two volumes to one project will be the first step in making you, the reader, an expert.

It is my hope that these books will be of value to the industrial student as well as the college student. In future I believe this material should be covered in undergraduate programs in business administration, engineering, science, medicine, and architecture. Arrow diagrams are as useful in the operating room as on the missile launching site.

A book of this nature incorporates recommendations, thoughts, and work of people other than the author. I am indebted to John J. McManus, Olin Mathieson Chemical Corporation, who constructively criticized the method of presentation; to Dr. Adrian McDonough, Professor of Industry, the Wharton School of Finance, University of Pennsylvania, for his guidance, encouragement, and moral support; to Dominic Fanelli, E. R. Squibb & Sons, and to Martin J. Gibson and E. S. Steben, Olin Mathieson Chemical Corporation, who commented on the manuscript; to Miss Catharine M. Haltigan, who typed it; and, most especially and appreciatively, to my wife Barbara, who suffered through the entire work with me. These two volumes are dedicated to her, the first woman in recorded history who had her wedding planned by PERT and CPM.

—R. L. M.
New York, 1964

Preface to Volume 1:
Finding the Critical Path

The basic elements of PERT and CPM are a network diagram and a critical path. The network is a model of the project as a whole created by linking together arrows representing specific jobs which must be done. The time required to perform each job is used to find the critical path, which is the longest chain (or chains) from a project's beginning to its completion.

The true value of these techniques becomes apparent only *after* the critical path has been found. Before applying PERT and CPM, therefore, the rules must be determined for creating network diagrams and finding the critical path. This volume is concerned with developing, explaining, and applying just these rules.

Contents

CHAPTER ONE: Introduction   13

PERT/CPM • Elements of a Project • Management—What Is It? • Computers and Mathematics • Why These Techniques? • What a Project Is

CHAPTER TWO: Arrow Diagrams   18

Arrow Representation • Linking Arrows • Deliveries and Lead Time • Logic Dummies • Events • Numbering Events • "Numbering" Dummies • Summary of Rules of Arrow Diagramming • Exercises • Solutions to Exercises

CHAPTER THREE: Diagramming a Project   43

A Chemical Plant Maintenance Project • Advantages • Decision Diagrams • Rules of Good Practice • Event Descriptions • Summary • Exercises

CHAPTER FOUR: Critical and Non-Critical Jobs—Earliest Start   58

Total Float • Earliest Starting Date of Each Activity • Sequence and Duration • Earliest Activity Start • Labeling and Other Conventions • Rules for Finding Earliest Activity Starts • The Quantity E • Earliest Start at Event 5 • Practical Procedure • The Last Event • Dummies • Summary • Exercises • Solutions

CHAPTER FIVE: Critical and Non-Critical Jobs—Latest Start   81

Train Analogy • Latest Activity Finish Times • Practical Procedure • Summary of Rules • Exercises • Solutions

CONTENTS

CHAPTER SIX: The Critical Path and Job Boundaries   97

*Activity Notation • Total Float • The Critical Path • Total Float and the
Critical Path • The Meaning of Total Float • Interfering Float and Event
Slack • Activity Orientation • Free Float • Independent Float • Summary
of Floats • Job Boundaries • Event Tables • Job Boundary Tables • Summary • Exercises • Solutions*

CHAPTER SEVEN: Milestone Networks   125

*The Pipeline Construction Project • The Critical Path • Observer and
Doer Requirements • Activity Orientation with Labeled Milestones • Detailed Event Networks • Summary*

CHAPTER EIGHT: Finding the Critical Path: A Perspective   138

*Finding the Plan and Schedule • Men and Machines Are Critical • The
New, Total Approach • Plan, Estimate, Revise • Finding the Critical Path
and Project Management*

CHAPTER ONE

Introduction

MANAGEMENT IS A TOUGH BUSINESS. Not only is the margin for error shrinking between success and failure, between profit and loss, but the things we manage often appear unmanageable. Rapid technological change, decreased profit margins, increased competition, a shorter lifespan for new products, and a faster tempo combine to make management more difficult and demanding.

To make effective decisions, managers must have available pertinent and timely information. The decision makers of today are constantly deluged by a vast sea of data. Often this information is disorganized and irrelevant to the problem at hand. The needed facts, even when present, are impossible to extract.

Before a decision is reached, certain specific questions should be raised. For example:

What are the alternative courses of action, if any?

What is the cost of each alternative?

What are the risks?

When must the decision be made?

What will be the consequences if the decision is delayed?

In managing projects—both large and small—failure to have the answers to these and other basic questions can be costly or even disastrous. The high and increasing costs of idle equipment, idle manpower, and lost time must be controlled. Ways must be found to develop better plans for projects, to allocate resources to project activities more economically, and to control all aspects of the projects more closely.

All this is true whether it concerns managing a business, supervising a research program, directing a voyage into space, or building one house. Many people recognize this problem of control, and many are working on its solution. PERT (Program Evaluation and Review Technique) and CPM (Critical Path Method) are project planning and control techniques that were developed to answer the basic needs of project management.

PERT/CPM   PERT and CPM were independently developed and first applied in the late 1950's. Initially, PERT was designed as a reporting technique to evaluate and monitor the phase-by-phase progress of the various projects (encompassing numerous contractors and subcontractors) in the Polaris missile program. CPM, on the other hand, was originally conceived as a computer-oriented planning technique designed to control construction, engineering, and plant maintenance projects.

Since PERT and CPM first appeared, their apparent differences have all but disappeared. In fact, features of one technique have been incorporated into the other, and vice versa. A difference that often used to be cited, for example, was that PERT was more suited to research and development projects in which more uncertainties were encountered. CPM was said to be especially effective in projects whose various jobs could be estimated in time and cost with a reasonable amount of accuracy—like the construction of a building. However, in recent years these differences, if they ever were valid ones, have disappeared.

The arrow diagram, or "network," is common to both methods. It is in the calculations that are made and in the emphasis that is placed on various aspects of the network that the differences appear. But, again, the variations between the way two users employ either PERT or CPM may be greater than the differences between the techniques themselves. The important point is that a working model of a project is developed by creating a master plan from which a realistic schedule can be prepared. This is true whichever method is used. The application of the basic approach, which can be termed operational planning, is more important than the specific rules by which the technique is applied (whether PERT or CPM).

Both techniques are equally applicable to planning, monitoring, and control, and both are equally applicable to *any* kind of project—R&D, construction, engineering, new product introduction, advertising campaigns, corporate planning, military tactical operations, and so on—provided the following concepts are continually borne in mind:

1. Planning must be geared to the operation to be performed; that is, the plan must be activity oriented. Attempting to plan with an event or "milestone" orientation can produce the *wrong* answer.

2. Reporting can be geared to the completion (whole or part) of

activities, or it can be geared to the arrival at, or expected date of arrival at, a milestone in the project. If an event orientation is selected for reporting purposes, then such a system can be properly established only from an activity-oriented plan.

This brief statement concerning the equal applicability of CPM and PERT is not perhaps convincing at this point. It will become obvious in later chapters.

There are three overall categories for the elements of a project:

Elements of a Project

1. Operations, or the things we *do*.

2. Resources, or the things we *use*.

3. The *conditions* or *restraints* under which we must work. These are the things outside our control.

Within these major elements there are certain characteristics or subclassifications that have to be considered. We are vitally concerned with the required sequence or order of operations. For example, it is fairly obvious that land must be leased or bought before building is started on it. However, if we are putting up two buildings side by side and we have only one excavating machine, it is not so obvious which hole should be dug first. The method of performing each operation must also be established. Associated with the method will be the time and cost of performance.

The resources are five in number: men, material, machines, money, and the one too often overlooked—time. These may be considered as *internal* restrictions. As to *externally* imposed conditions, a predetermined and necessary completion date is our greatest concern. Another external restraint may be capital restrictions of one kind or another. Quite obviously, any project plan must take into account the delivery by outside agencies of such things as design, materials, machines, and the like. Approvals, inspections, and just about anything else that can be thought of may likewise be called outside restrictions.

All these elements and subelements compose the project. The objective is to coordinate all of them—often conflicting—in a master plan which must be a working model of the project.

The first step in creating such a master plan is to determine what jobs are to be done and their sequence of performance. This is best carried out by producing an arrow, or network, diagram.

Before outlining in greater detail how PERT/CPM can be applied to project management problems, let us take a look at management. Just exactly what is it? It obviously means many things to many people. For instance, making a profit in a corporation, passing an examination, winning a battle, or preparing a budget all require management. Here are four diverse activities, yet management can be generalized to cover each one of these and all others we can think of.

Management— What Is It?

Essentially, management can be defined as—

1. Selecting the objectives of our enterprise (or project).
2. Determining what is required to meet these objectives.
3. *Judiciously* allocating the resources at our disposal to achieve these objectives according to a plan and schedule.
4. Controlling the entire process from point of decision or commitment to completion (achievement of objectives).

Its effectiveness is measured by the results it achieves and, more especially, by the response time of manager and method when things go wrong.

Quite obviously, planning is a vital function of management. However, there is the equally vital and more specific task of planning, scheduling, and supervising the various individual projects which are integral parts of an overall plan. Efficient planning of these constituent projects *always* means the difference between "on time" and "late," and it *can* mean the difference between success and failure.

Computers and Mathematics

Network analysis was developed as a computer-oriented project planning, scheduling, and control technique through the use of higher mathematics. The terms "mathematics" and "computer" do not, in any way, restrict CPM and PERT. The computer is a tool. While CPM and PERT calculations are often produced by computer, they can just as well be figured by hand. The only time a computer should be used is when speed is required for a large mass of calculations, or when it is cheaper.

Mathematics is not used in applying CPM and PERT, nor is any knowledge of mathematics required to apply these tools. Mathematics is used to develop, justify, and prove the rules, *which require only simple arithmetic to apply,* or which are programed into a computer.

In summary, mathematics justifies the rules, and computers can speed the result. We don't really need to know anything further about either.

Why These Techniques?

Just how and why are CPM and PERT applied to a project? The "why" is obvious. Decisions often commit a company to major outlays of capital. The projects such decisions set in motion lead to a need to coordinate the myriad interrelated functions that must be considered to produce a plan and schedule. Even more important is the need to be able to incorporate changes, as they occur, and immediately to know the effect of a change. What is required, therefore, is a dynamic planning and scheduling system which will not only produce the best possible initial plan and schedule but will be sufficiently dynamic to react instantaneously to changed conditions and still produce the best plan and schedule.

What a Project Is

Prior to outlining how network analysis is applied to project management, it is necessary to consider some additional basic concepts.

First, just exactly what is a project? Erecting a building is a project, but how do we define a project? A project is any task which has a definable beginning and a definable end and requires the expenditure of one or more resources in each of the separate but interrelated and interdependent activities which must be completed to achieve the objectives for which the task (or project) was instituted. In this sense, for example, the creation and development, tooling up, and introduction of a new product is a "project" (and each element can be considered a "subproject"). The regular manufacture and sale of a product after introduction would be considered *not* a "project" but rather a cyclic process. PERT and CPM, as such, are not directly applicable to the continuous or cyclic type of project. Other techniques are of greater value in this connection.

CHAPTER TWO

Arrow Diagrams

We MAY DEFINE PLANNING as the determination of required resources and their order of commitment in each of the various but interrelated activities of a project. In planning a project, then, the first step is to establish the necessary operations or activities to be performed, and subsequently to determine their necessary sequence, or order of performance. Various means have been used and are being used to determine work sequence. The result is a model, on paper, of the manner in which the project will be carried out. If the model is a good one, it can serve as a working tool; if not, it is virtually valueless, and problems must be solved as they occur.

A common technique for finding the proper work sequence is to make a list of the activities and with the aid of this list to rearrange all the activities in their order of performance. This is not only tedious but also cumbersome, requiring as it does a great deal of writing and rearranging. More important, however, it is quite prone to error. Furthermore, such a list is often of little real day-to-day operational value for a number of reasons. Among them:

1. There is a distinct possibility of omission, especially in large projects.

2. Surrounded by detail, the planner may sequence the work as it was done in the past, or by intuition, rather than by determining the *necessary* sequence.

3. Very often there is no attempt to solve problems before they occur.

4. The reasoning behind the resulting sequence is not readily apparent to other people and is often forgotten by the planner himself.

To overcome these disadvantages a more convenient means of creating a project model has been devised. This is called "arrow diagramming" or "network diagramming." The result of this technique, an arrow diagram, is a realistic working model of the project. It has many advantages, which we shall explore presently.

Arrow Representation

A representation is required in any modeling procedure. For instance, when making a replica of a building, often a scale measure of one inch is used in the model to represent one foot of the actual building. In modeling a project, however, the representation is not exactly of the same kind. We create, not a "scale" model as such, but a "logic" model.

In arrow diagramming the standard of representation is an arrow, as shown in Figure 1. The length of the arrow is immaterial; the direction in which it points is immaterial. The only significant fact is that the arrow represents something that has to be done—the job, the operation, the activity, or whatever. The tail of the arrow represents the commencement of the activity, and the head represents its completion. Hence, what we really have is a means of showing the flow of time, from the beginning to the end of some activity. Since this is a "logic" model, the scale is of no consequence.

As shown in Figure 1, we begin by representing the function of placing pipe in a trench as an arrow. This operation is part of the project of building a pipeline, and the arrow is labeled "LAY PIPE."* It would be rather ridiculous if the same task were represented by more than one arrow. Doing this would be equivalent to listing the same job twice on a procedure. To eliminate this possibility the restriction is made that each arrow is unique, and any single activity *cannot* be represented by more than one arrow.

Equivalent versions of the representation by an arrow of the job of "lay pipe":

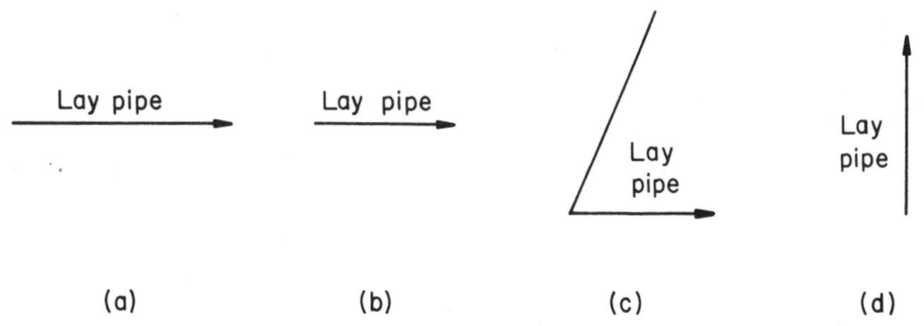

FIGURE 1

(a)   (b)   (c)   (d)

*It is normally better to be specific rather than to speak in generalities, and for that reason the development of the rules of arrow diagramming will be illustrated by reference to a specific project. The project selected is that of building a long pipeline, and we shall term it Project 300. While any type of project (shipbuilding, R&D, new product introduction, and so on) could have served, the pipeline project was selected because the linkages between its operations should be readily understood by all. This would not necessarily be true of other projects for which specialized knowledge is required to appreciate the job interrelationships.

Thus, the first rule of arrow diagramming is:

Rule 1(a)

One and only one arrow is used to represent the operation to be performed. The length of the arrow and the direction in which it points have no significance.

Linking Arrows

Following the adoption of this means of representation, the next step is to relate the various operations or jobs required to complete the project. This is equivalent to connecting the arrows into a network which represents the project at hand.

Let's consider an overall simplified approach to the project of building a long pipeline. The requirements are to dig a trench, lay the pipe inside it, weld and pressure-test the sections, and then fill the trench. For this project, then, there are four operations: trench, lay pipe, weld and test, and backfill. Each of these four operations can be represented by an arrow. In the case of the pipelaying operation, as shown in Figure 1, we ask, "What immediately precedes (or at least must come before) this operation?" It is readily evident that digging the hole, or trenching, must be done before the pipe can be placed in the trench. This fact may be depicted as shown in Figure 2.

FIGURE 2

The trench *must* be dug before the pipe can be placed in it:

Trench   Lay pipe

This leads to another rule of arrow diagramming:

Rule 2(a)

Arrows are connected to form a model of the project by answering, for each operation, the question, "What immediately precedes this operation?"

The next step may readily be guessed. Having answered the question, "What precedes?" we are naturally inclined to ask, "What follows?" Once again, taking the example of laying pipe, the only action that *can* follow is to weld the sections together and to test the weld; that is, "(weld and test)" follows "(lay pipe)." It is the same as asking, for the "(weld and test)" operation, "What must precede?" This step is depicted in Figure 3.

FIGURE 3

The "weld and test" operation follows the "lay pipe" activity:

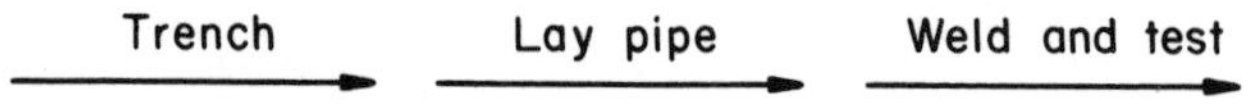

Trench   Lay pipe   Weld and test

It may be stated in rule form as follows:

Rule 2(b)

Arrows are connected to form arrow diagram models of the project by answering, for each operation, the question, "What follows?"

By applying the rules outlined so far, the whole project of constructing a pipeline may be modeled as shown in Figure 4.

Project 300. Simplified arrow diagram of a pipeline construction project:

FIGURE 4

Trench   Lay pipe   Weld and test   Backfill

A close study of Figure 4 will reveal certain inadequacies. If we are practical, we realize that if the pipeline is 200 miles long, we do not have to trench for 200 miles before we can place a single piece of pipe. We can dig a certain amount of trench and begin placing pipe in it while continuing the trenching activity ahead of the pipelaying operation. Since this is a practical way of building a pipeline, let us see how we represent it in our model. Figure 5 shows that we can consider some overall function, such as trenching, to be composed of various segmented work phases. For instance, the first section that must be trenched before any pipe can be placed in it can be very simply labeled "(trench first part)." The remainder of the trenching operation can be labeled "(trench to completion)." Such labels do not imply *how much* trenching must be done, they merely indicate the fact that *some* trenching must be done before pipelaying can begin. The operations of pipelaying and completing the trenching are thus, not necessarily concurrent in time, but concurrent in the sense that both operations require some trenching to be completed. While the pipelaying operation could be started at the same time as the trenching continues, there is no limitation or imposition requiring that this be so.

An illustration of the use of multiple arrows for the same function:

FIGURE 5

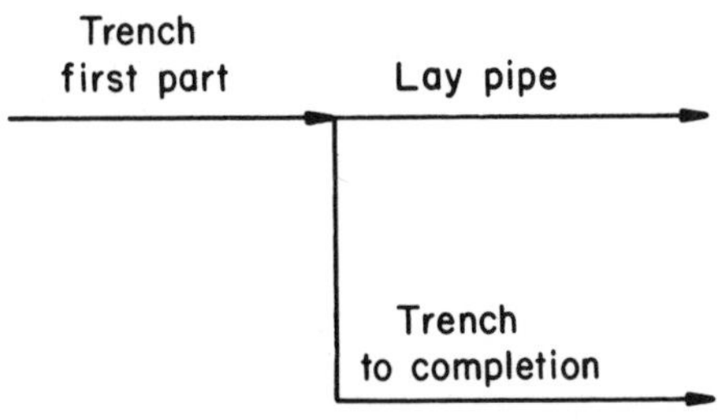

Trench
first part   Lay pipe

Trench
to completion

This particular case points up two additional aspects of the first two rules of arrow diagramming. The first of these concerns the linking of arrows (to form arrow diagrams) when jobs are concurrent, which may be stated as follows:

> *Arrows are connected to form arrow diagram models of a project by answering, for each operation, the question, "What is concurrent (that is, what other jobs depend on exactly the same preceding jobs as the one in question)?"*

Rule 2(c)

In addition, we have established another aspect of the first rule pertaining to representation:

Functions, operations, or jobs may be broken up and represented by a number of arrows. (This does not invalidate the Rule 1(a) which specifies that each arrow is unique. Even if a number of arrows are used to represent different parts of the same operation, each arrow is still unique because it represents exactly one, and only one, segment of the overall task.)

With these additional rules, the arrow diagram for the pipeline project can become much more realistic. The result of phasing for linking the start of activities is shown in Figure 6.

FIGURE 6   Phasing the operations:

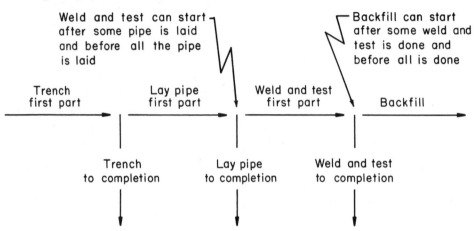

In Figure 6 the phasing is shown for all the operations except (backfill). However, the diagram at this stage is incomplete, since there are "ending" linkages similar to the "start" linkages. For example, all the pipe cannot be placed until all the trenching is completed, as is shown in Figure 7.

FIGURE 7   Ending linkage for the trenching operation:

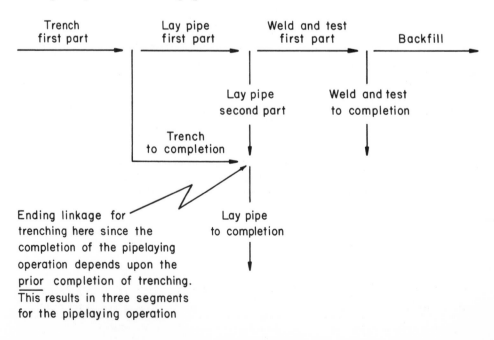

22

Using this approach, the "ending" linkages for the (weld and test) and (backfill) operations are developed as shown in Figure 8.

Project 300. More realistic diagram of the pipeline project:

FIGURE 8

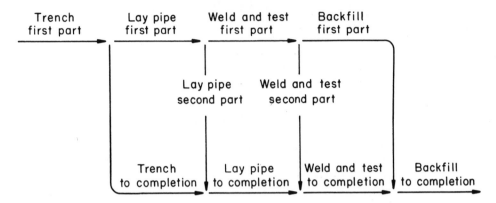

So far in our analysis of the pipeline project we have considered only the work to be done. What about the material? Certainly we must have pipe available before we can place the first length of pipe.

Deliveries and Lead Time

Deliveries, which are restraints on our project, are represented in the model as arrows, since they are activities which are directly related to the completion of the project. As a result, the first rule of arrow diagramming is understood to include deliveries as operations to be represented as arrows. The use of arrows to represent the delivery of pipe is shown in Figure 9.

Deliveries of material are represented as arrows:

FIGURE 9

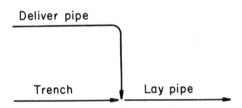

Obviously, not *all* the pipe must be delivered before the pipelaying operation can begin, but *all* the pipe must be delivered *before* all the pipe can be placed.

Let us now build this fact into our model, or arrow diagram, as shown in Figure 10.

A possible diagram:

FIGURE 10

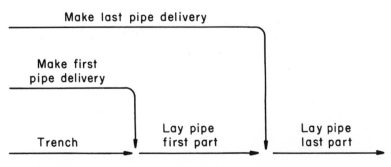

Diagramming the situation in this fashion leaves something to be desired. First, where do all the arrows start?

This fault can be overcome by introducing a single "start" or (lead time) arrow to show all previous work or, at least, to indicate a starting point for all arrows. Hence, still another rule of arrow diagramming is:

Rule 3

> **It is good practice to start all diagrams with a single arrow marked "(lead time)" and to show all actual "work" arrows starting after "(lead time)."**

The use of lead time is shown in Figure 11.

FIGURE 11   Introducing lead time as a project starting point:

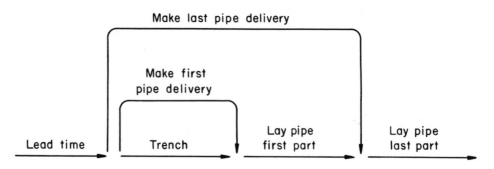

Logic Dummies

Even though this is more satisfactory, a problem still exists. In an actual pipeline construction project the placing of pipe can begin, as we know, before *all* the trenching is done. This is shown incorrectly in Figure 12.

FIGURE 12   An incorrect attempt to link deliveries to the work to be done:

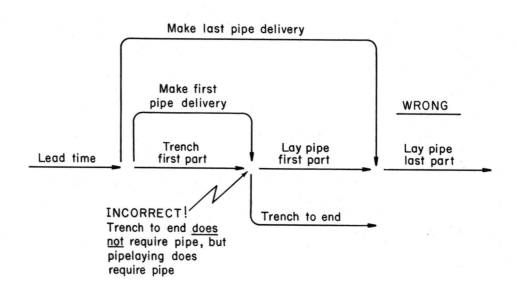

It is evident from the diagram that its logic is incorrect. What is really intended is the situation depicted in Figure 13.

Correct model of pipe delivery situation:

FIGURE 13

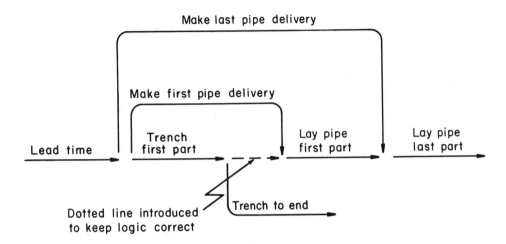

The logic in Figure 13 is now correct; the dotted line shows that *some trenching* and *some pipe* are required before pipelaying can start but that *no pipe* is required to keep the trenching operation going. The dotted line is called a "dummy" since it does not exist—it takes no time and costs nothing—but it is a definite logical restriction. The dummy is employed to keep the logical sequencing of jobs, and their interrelationship, correct.

The introduction of the dummy may be further exemplified by the following situation. Consider a project consisting of four jobs: *A*, *B*, *C*, and *D*. The start of job *B* depends solely upon the completion of job *A;* the start of job *D* depends on the completion of both jobs *A* and *C*. The problem is to draw the arrow diagram. The diagram as shown in Figure 14 is incorrect, since we cannot have two arrows representing the same job (*A*).

Incorrect since two arrows *cannot* be used to represent the same thing:

FIGURE 14

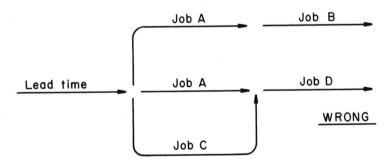

The nature of this error is evident when we refer to the pipeline project (see Figure 15).

FIGURE 15   Two arrows both symbolizing the "trench first part" activity are *incorrect*:

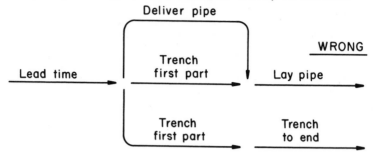

Another approach to the "*ABCD*" problem is to draw the diagram as shown in Figure 16. This is also incorrect, since it indicates that job *B* depends on both jobs *A* and *C* being done, whereas job *B* depends only on job *A*.

FIGURE 16   Incorrect diagram, since job *B* depends *only* on job *A* being done:

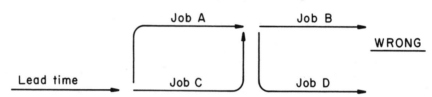

The correct diagram for the "*ABCD*" problem can be produced *only* by introducing the dummy job *E* as shown in Figure 17.

FIGURE 17   Introducing dummy job *E* makes logic correct:

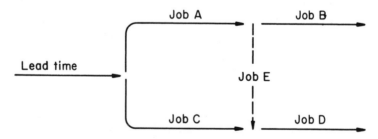

With the use of the dummy, the logic is corrected and diagrams can be produced that are more realistic. It may help to think of dummies in arrow diagrams as being as important and as useful as the zero of arithmetic. Could you add, subtract, multiply, or divide without a zero? You could if you used Roman numerals, but it would be awkward, to say the least.

Using dummies and employing the rules of arrow diagramming discussed thus far, we show in Figure 18 a simplified model of the pipeline project. A formal rule for using dummies will be stated later.

Project 300. Correct, though simplified, diagram of a pipeline construction project:

FIGURE 18

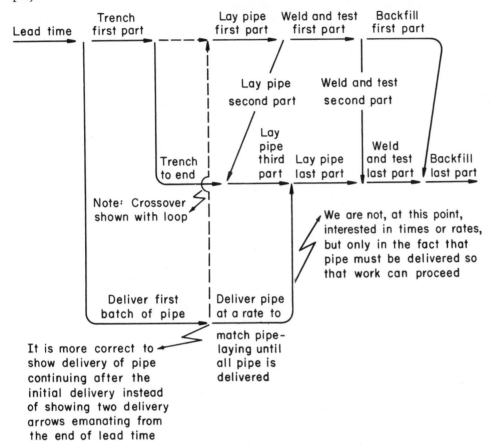

As shown in Figure 19, arrows represent functions that consume time. The junction of arrows is a point in time and, as such, does not consume time. It represents that point in time when all jobs ending at the point are done, and all succeeding jobs that begin at that point can start. All junction points, or nodes, are called "events"; they are the points in time when we finish some one piece of work and start another.

Events

Concept of an event as a junction of activities:

FIGURE 19

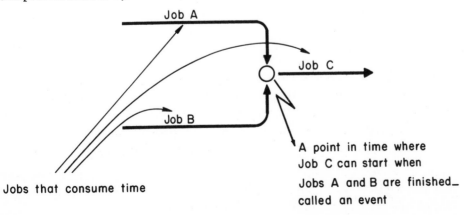

Numbering Events

If we number these junction points, or events, we can thus describe activities by the event numbers between which they lie. Up to this point, we have labeled the arrows with statements to describe the activities they represent. In Figure 20, numbers have been placed at the junction points of arrows. By referring to the numbers we can refer to the activity of (trench first part) as job (2,3).

Similarly, job (3,5) is the dummy which shows that (trench to end) [job (3,7)] does not require any pipe delivery [job (2,4)], whereas (lay pipe first part) [job (5,6)] does.

Being able to represent an activity in numeric form has many advantages. The main ones are:

1. Selection is immediate; looking at the diagram, it is easier to pick out numbers than words. For example, finding job (6,8) is more readily achieved than searching through all the descriptions to find (weld and test first part).

2. Reference is abbreviated, but exact; for example, writing or saying job (6,8) is certainly simpler than using the phrase "(weld and test first part)." And yet the meaning is exactly known since that is exactly what job (6,8) is.

3. Sequence is immediately evident; for instance, job (5,6) precedes jobs (6,7) and (6,8); or job (6,7) is concurrent with job (6,8); or jobs (8,10) and (8,11) follow job (6,8); and so on.

4. Reference to sequential jobs is easier; to say, "(Backfill first part) and (weld and test second part) can start when (weld and test first part) is finished," is a little more cumbersome than the phrasing, "Jobs (8,10) and (8,11) can start when job (6,8) is finished." Similarly, in taking a sequence of jobs from beginning to end, it is simpler to describe them as jobs (1,2), (2,4), (4,9), (9,10), (10,11), and (11,12) than to use the longwinded phrasing, "(Lead time), (deliver pipe first batch), (deliver pipe to end), (lay pipe to end), (weld and test to end), and (backfill to end)." The numeric "chain" not only is easier to set out, it is also much more meaningful.

Thus, using numbers at the junction points of arrows is helpful. Let us consider the numbering of junction points, or events, in more detail.

We could indiscriminately number events at random, and, actually, there is no reason why we cannot or should not. If, looking ahead, we wish to use an electronic computer to process the arithmetic procedures that are required, the computer could, if necessary, renumber the events in any fashion. On the other hand, if no computer is used and all arithmetic calculations are performed "by hand" (really "by head"), then there is still no logical reason to number events in any specific fashion. Experience has shown, however, that numbering events in a special manner makes the arithmetic procedure simpler. For this reason only—convenience and *not* logic—another rule is imposed.

FIGURE 20

Project 300. Numbers at junction points of arrows simplify job reference:

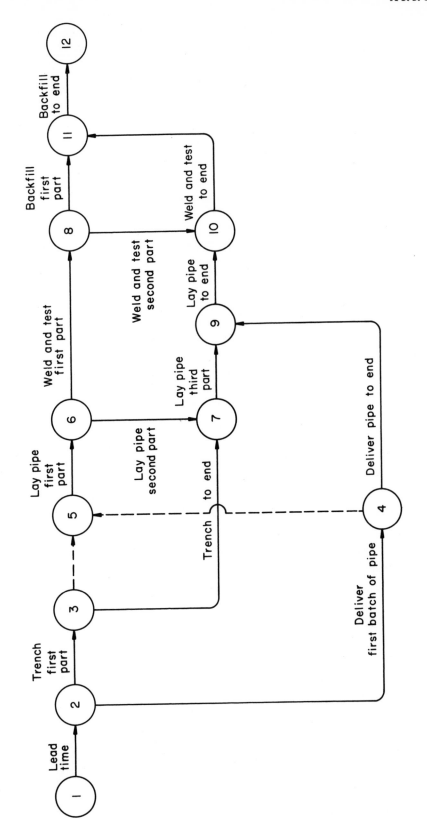

<u>*Rule 4*</u>

Junctions of arrows are called events. They are points in time, and consume no time. They are numbered to provide a convenient numeric sequential designation for all activities (arrows). It is good practice to number events in such fashion that the number at the tail of any arrow is always smaller than the number at the head of each arrow.

It is common practice to label the first event 1, and then to progress through the network labeling subsequent events consecutively. Variations of this common practice are considered in the next chapter.

In Project 301, Figure 21, the first event has been labeled 1.

FIGURE 21

Project 301:

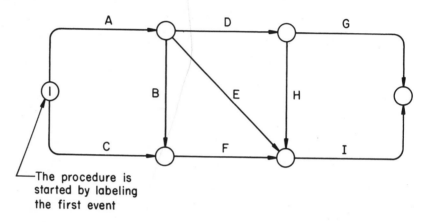

└─The procedure is started by labeling the first event

The next step is to label some event with the number 2. Two jobs, *A* and *C*, proceed from event 1. At least one of them will end at some event that we can number.

Consider job *C*. It ends at the event where job *F* starts. At this event the number 2 cannot be placed since a job ends there—that is, job *B*—which does not have the starting event (the event at the tail of the arrow representing job *B*) numbered.

Job *A* ends at the event where jobs *B*, *D*, and *E* start. All the jobs that end there (in this case job *A* only) have "their tails numbered" (in this case event 1 is labeled). Hence, this event *can* be numbered next. It is labeled 2.

FIGURE 22

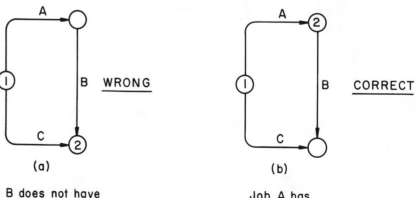

(a)

Job B does not have its tail event labeled

(b)

Job A has tail labeled

The same procedure is followed to label an event with the number 3. In this case, two possibilities exist which are both correct, as is shown in Figure 23.

Project 301. Two correct versions of numbering:

FIGURE 23

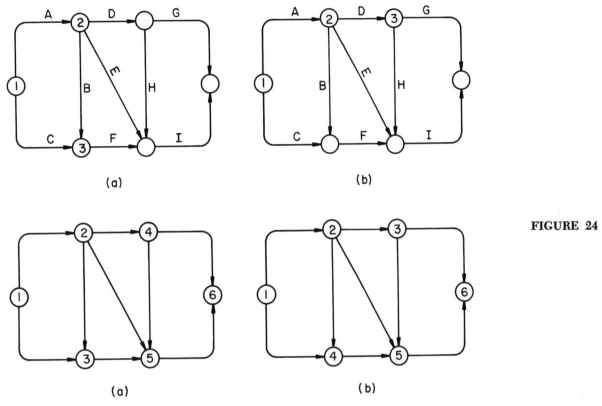

(a)   (b)

FIGURE 24

(a)   (b)

In Project 301, as shown in Figures 23 and 24, there is some variation possible. Consider now Project 302 in Figure 25, where no variation whatsoever is possible.

Project 302. No variation in numbering events is possible because there is only *one* correct answer:

FIGURE 25

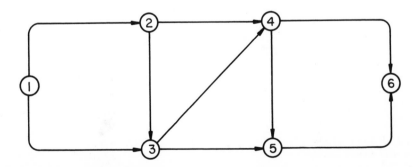

"Numbering" Dummies

Next consider the case of Project 303, shown in Figure 26.

FIGURE 26

Project 303. Which of jobs *B*, *C*, or *D* is understood by referring to job (2,3)?

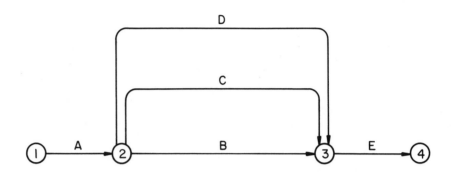

A study will reveal that while the number at the tail is smaller than the number at the head of an arrow, there are three jobs (*B*, *C*, and *D*) labeled (2,3). Our objective is to keep activity designation in terms of event numbers unique. If this is not done, many advantages of event numbering are lost.

To overcome the difficulty, dummies are used. As shown in Figure 27, dummies provide the unique designation of job (2,3) for *D*, job (2,4) for *C*, and job (2,5) for *B*.

In Figure 27 the dummies are placed at the ends of jobs *C* and *D*. It is also correct, however, to place them before, as we prefer. All the possibilities shown in Figure 28 are, in fact, equally correct.

FIGURE 27

Project 303. Dummies introduced to guarantee the unique designations job (2,3) for *D*, job (2,4) for *C*, and job (2,5) for *B*:

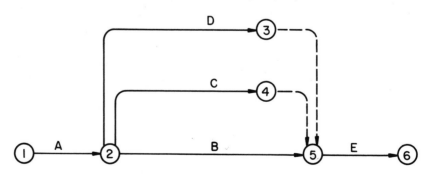

Both versions are correct. Furthermore, they are still correct if event numbers 3 and 4 are interchanged:

FIGURE 28

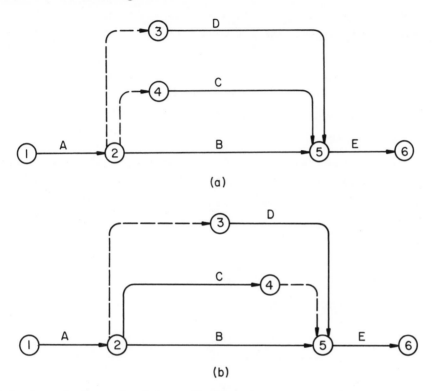

(a)

(b)

This leads to the last rule of arrow diagramming:

Dummies are jobs that have no duration or cost. They are introduced
(1) to keep the logic correct, and
(2) to keep unique the numeric designation for event numbers at the tail and head of each arrow.

Rule 5

The rules of modeling a project (arrow diagramming) may be summarized as follows:

Summary of Rules of Arrow Diagramming

RULE 1. Each activity or job (actual operation or a delivery) is represented by an arrow.

FIGURE 29

One, and only one, arrow can be used to represent each job. However, a job may be segmented and represented by a number of arrows. Thus:

FIGURE 30

The length of the arrow and the direction in which it points are unimportant. Each arrow indicates the existence of some operation, or specific segment of an operation, and time flows from the tail to the head of the arrow, representing the elapsed time and work from start to finish (tail to head).

RULE 2. An arrow diagram (or model of the project) is created by connecting arrows. This is done by considering, for each arrow, three questions:

- What precedes?
- What follows?
- What can be concurrent? (That is, what other jobs, if any, depend only on the same ones that precede the current job in question?)

Restraints of any kind, such as deliveries on a construction project, are also drawn as arrows.

FIGURE 31

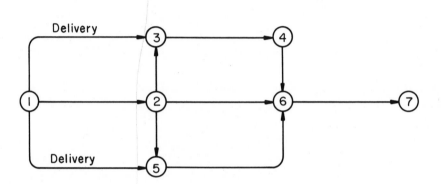

RULE 3. It is good practice to start each diagram with an arrow labeled "lead time." This is to take care of the multitudinous little things which must be done before a project is started. Lead time may or may not later be given a duration.

FIGURE 32

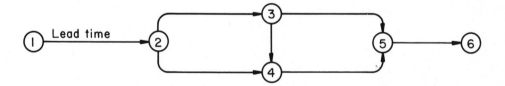

RULE 4. Since arrows represent jobs or activities that take time, the junctions of arrows represent positions in time when all previous jobs are done and succeeding ones can start. These points in time are called "events." Similarly, events exist at the start and end of each job.

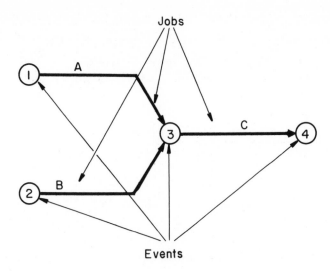

Jobs

Events

When the arrow diagram is complete, all the events are numbered. Thus, instead of referring to a job by an alphabetical description, its "event pair" can be used. For example, in Figure 34, job A can be represented by (2,3), B as (3,4), and so on. As a result, each arrow has a unique "number pair" representation.

The numbering of events should be such that the number at the head of the arrow is always larger than the number at its tail. The numbers need not be consecutive and need not start with 1.

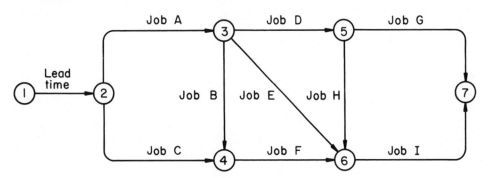

FIGURE 34

RULE 5. Artificial jobs, or "dummies," are introduced when necessary to keep our logic or numbering systems unique.

(a) Logic

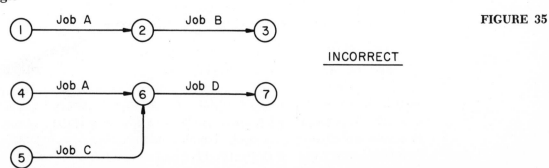

FIGURE 35

INCORRECT

Here job B depends on A being done, while D depends on both A and C being done. In Figure 35 we have two arrows for job A. This violates the first rule of arrow diagramming, and it is wrong. If we represent this problem as shown in Figure 36, we are also wrong since we show B dependent on C as well as A, and this is not so.

FIGURE 36

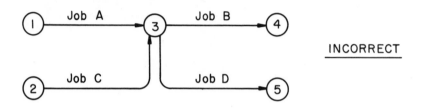

INCORRECT

The correct logic is shown by introducing job E, as shown in Figure 37.

FIGURE 37

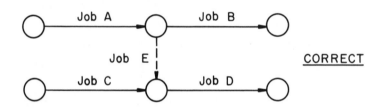

CORRECT

Job E is called a dummy since it has no duration or cost and really doesn't exist. However, with job E present in the diagram, the *logic* becomes correct.

(b) Numbering

In Figure 38 it is shown that three jobs, B, C, and D, can be represented by the event pair designation (2,3).

FIGURE 38

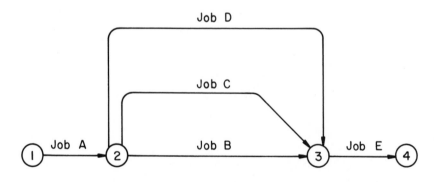

The rule for numbering events was established mainly to provide, for each arrow (or job it represents), a unique number pair designation. To provide such unique representation, dummies are used when necessary. The use of dummies for Figure 38 is shown in Figure 39, where (3,5) and (4,5) are dummies introduced to provide the unique designations (2,5) for job B, (2,3) for job C, and (2,4) for job D.

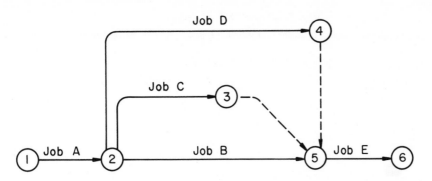

1. Number the events in the following projects. (Note that job descriptions are omitted for simplicity.)

(a) Project 304:

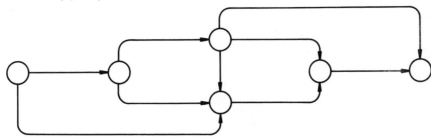

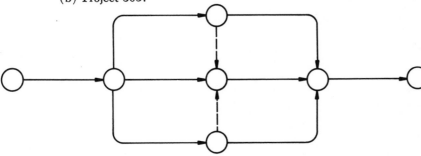

(b) Project 305:

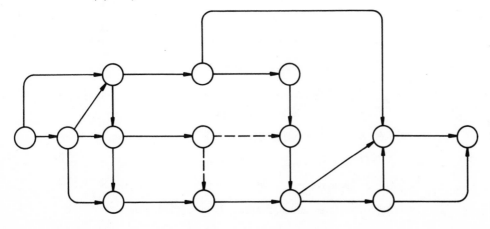

(c) Project 306:

37

2. Determine whether any of the dummies shown in the following diagrams are *not* really needed. (That is, do superfluous dummies exist?)

(a) Project 307:

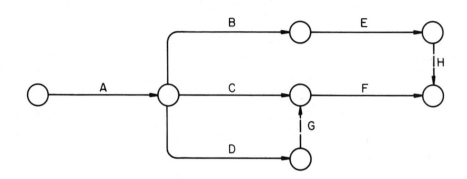

(b) Project 308:

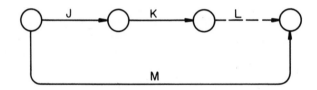

(c) Project 309:

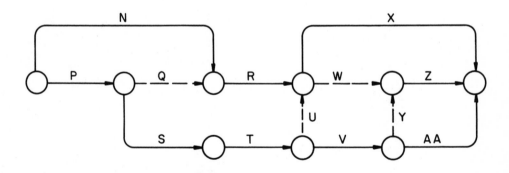

3. A project, No. 310, consists of six jobs, A, B, C, D, E, and F. Draw the arrow diagram and number the events if—

(a) Jobs B and C depend only on A.

(b) Job D depends on B, but not on C.

(c) Job E depends on C and B.

(d) The project is complete when D and E are done.

4. A project, No. 311, consists of eight jobs, *M, N, O, P, Q, R, S,* and *T.* Draw the arrow diagram and number the events if—

(a) Jobs *M, N,* and *Q* can start immediately.

(b) Jobs *O* and *P* are concurrent and depend on the completion of both *M* and *N.*

(c) Jobs *R* and *S* are concurrent and depend on the completion of *O.*

(d) Job *T* depends on the completion of jobs *P, Q,* and *R.*

(e) The project is complete when *S* and *T* are done.

5. Assume that you are driving a car and get a flat tire. The problem is to change the tire and drive on. A list has been prepared of activities associated with changing the flat tire. They are *not* necessarily listed in the required sequence of performance. Draw the arrow diagram for this project, No. 312, using the list of activities given.

NOTE 1. The number of people in the car is of no consequence since we are *planning.* The resource availability (people in the car or on hand when the car stops) is a factor only in *scheduling,* which takes place only after the plan is complete. Since arrow diagramming is just the first step in producing a plan, the number of people available *must not* be considered in preparing the arrow diagram for changing a flat tire.

NOTE 2. In preparing your diagram, do not fragment any of the activities listed. While the result will not be as accurate, it will still serve to acquire familiarity with the rules of arrow diagramming.

Project 312. List of activities for flat-tire problem:

1. Lead time—stop car.
2. Get spare tire.
3. Loosen lugs.
4. Jack up car.
5. Put on spare.
6. Lower car.
7. Get screwdriver for use in removing hubcap.
8. Remove hubcap.
9. Replace lugs.
10. Put flat in trunk.
11. Tighten lugs.
12. Open trunk.
13. Get jack.
14. Position jack.
15. Replace screwdriver.
16. Get lug wrench.
17. Remove lugs.
18. Replace hubcap.
19. Replace wrench.
20. Close trunk.
21. Replace jack.
22. Remove flat.
23. Drive off safely.

NOTE: The screwdriver, spare, lug wrench, and jack are all in the trunk of the car.

1. (a) Project 304:

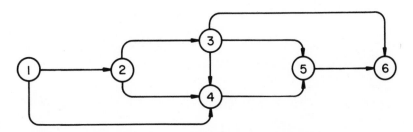

Note that only one solution is possible.

(b) Project 305:

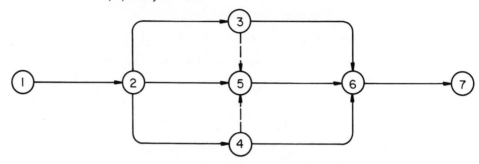

Note that only one solution is possible and that no unique designation for each job would be possible without dummies (3,5) and (4,5).

(c) Project 306:

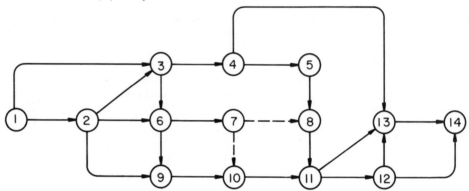

In this case a number of solutions are possible. It is good practice (not essential but helpful), however, to number along the top of the diagram as far as you can go and then to come down to the next row and go along, and so on.

2. (a) Project 307:

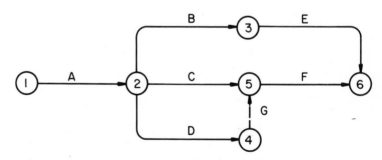

Dummy H is not needed since job F can continue directly into event 6.

Dummy G, on the other hand, is required to give jobs C and D the unique designations (2,5) and (2,4), respectively.

(b) Project 308:

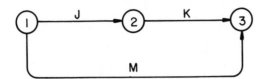

Dummy *L* is superfluous.

(c) Project 309:

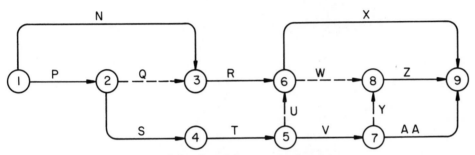

None of the dummies is superfluous.

NOTE: The key factor here is that job *X* requires the completion of jobs *R* and *T* but *not* of *V*. Hence, all dummies are required.

3. Project 310:

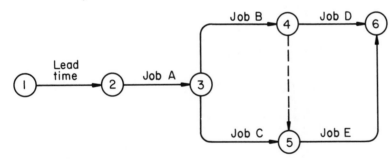

4. Project 311:

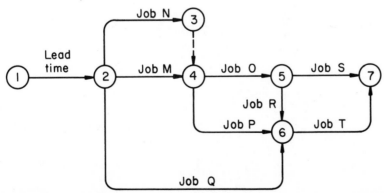

5. Project 312. Arrow diagram for changing a flat tire:

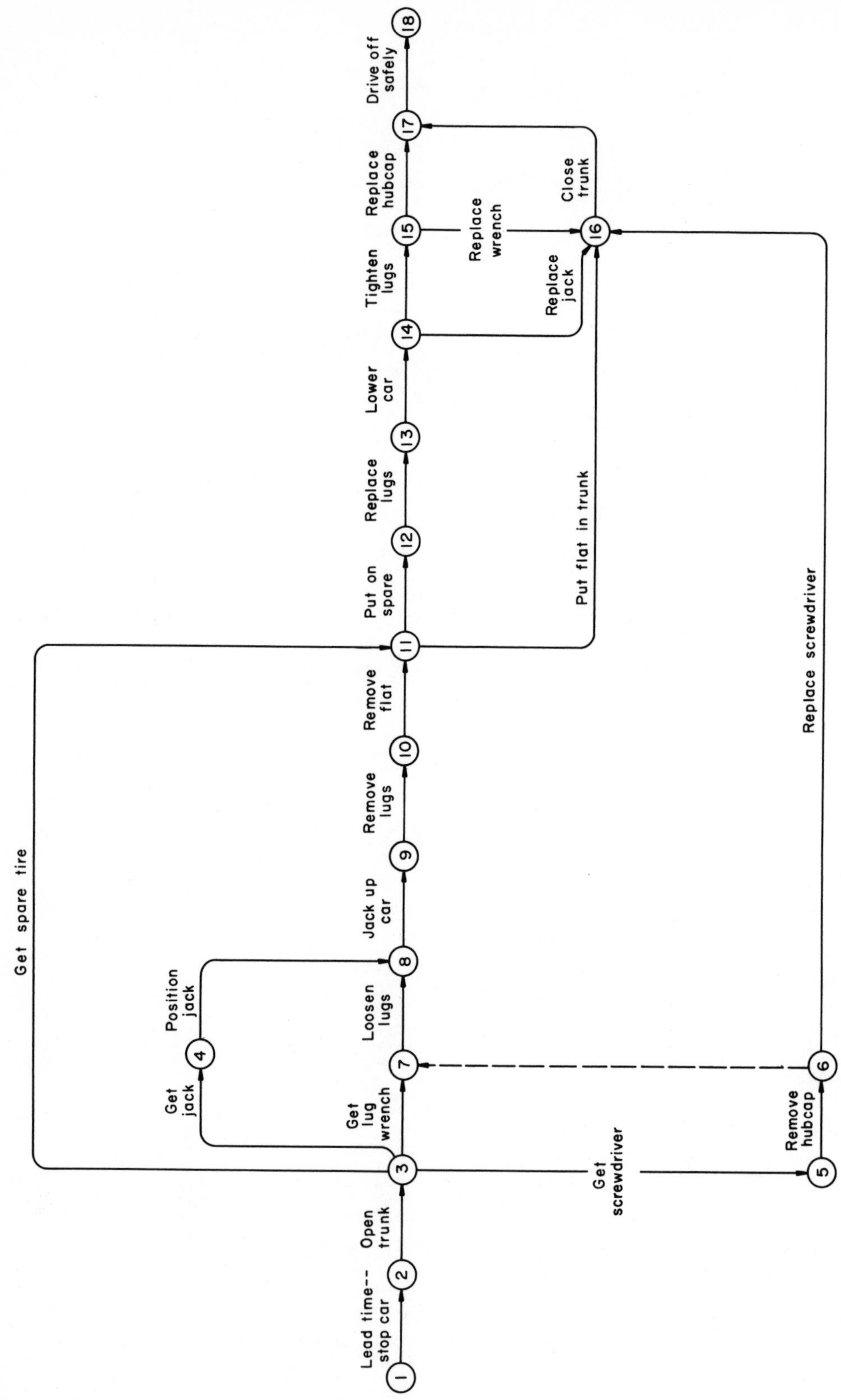

CHAPTER THREE

Diagramming a Project

Now THAT THE RULES OF arrow diagramming have been developed, let us illustrate the manner in which they are applied to a project. Any type of project—R&D, advertising, setting up a production line, and so on—could serve. However, once again a project of "general" nature, understandable to everyone, has been selected. This particular selection should not lead to any assumption that the range of application for the arrow diagramming technique is limited. The large number and variety of successful case histories to date prove that arrow diagramming can be gainfully and profitably applied to *any* project—large or small.

Consider the following project. Some overhead piping must be replaced in a chemical plant. There are a number of valves at floor level associated with this particular section of the pipeline, and we know that some valves are defective. The project calls for removing the old pipe and valves, putting new pipe and valves in place, insulating the pipe, and then cleaning up.

A Chemical Plant Maintenance Project

Now to diagram the problem.

The best way to start is to jot down some of the easily determinable things to be done—and *not* in any order. From a description of this project (let's call it No. 400), we know that the following things must be done:

1. Erect, and later dismantle, a scaffold.
2. Remove the old pipe and valves.
3. Put the new pipe and valves in place.
4. Deactivate the old line and disconnect the valves.
5. Measure and sketch the work to be done.

6. Order the materials.
7. Prefabricate the pipe sections prior to putting them in place.
8. Insulate the new pipeline.
9. Test the new line.
10. Assemble the work crew.

The next step is to start drawing the diagram. No attempt is made to order the list (put it in sequence) or check it for completeness. The arrow diagramming procedure will do that for us better than we can by listing. The real purpose in putting down the short list of activities is to get us to thinking in terms of the major functions or operations that are needed to complete the project.

The diagramming starts by drawing the lead time arrow and putting down all the things that can be done immediately. As shown in Figure 1, the only things we can do are to assemble the crew and to stop using the old line. Actually, when we come to schedule this project, the old line will be used as long as possible. Logically, however, we *could* stop using it immediately. For that reason it is drawn in as shown.

FIGURE 1

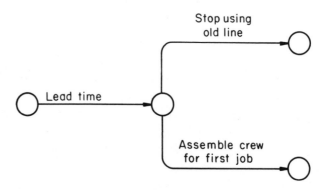

It is good practice to draw arrows as shown in Figure 1 so that the final diagram has a cigar or submarine shape. This presents a better-looking diagram than the equally correct straight-line approach of Figure 2.

FIGURE 2

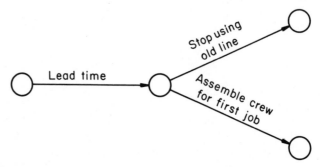

Considering Project 400 once more, we continue the work sequence after assembling the crew. As shown in Figure 3, the first thing we do is to measure and sketch the old line; then we develop a list of materials. With this list we can go ahead and erect the scaffold (using materials immediately available at hand), order the pipe, and order the valves. We do not have to erect the scaffold before measuring the old line, since this job can readily be done by using stepladders, which are always available. There is no need to show the use of stepladders, however, since that would be trivial. We always omit unnecessary detail but always include *required* detail, no matter how small.

The situation to this point is shown in Figure 3.

FIGURE 3

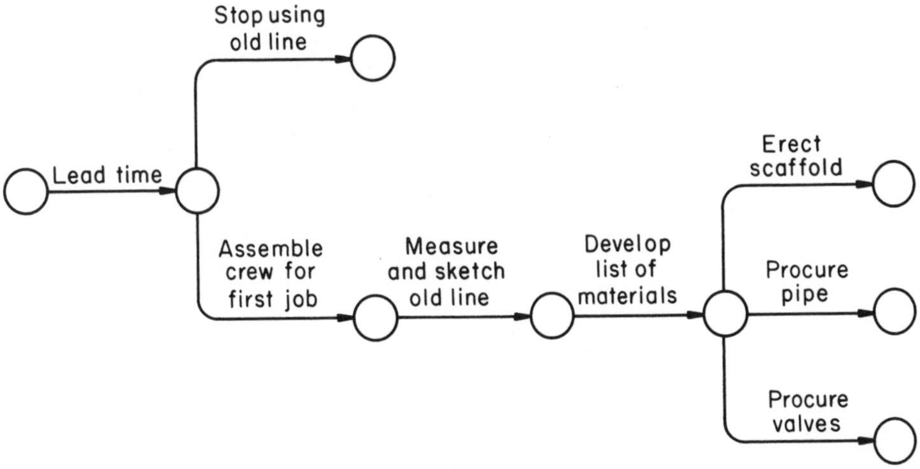

After the pipe is procured, new pipe sections can be prefabricated and put in place. However, the old pipe has to be removed first, which requires two prior jobs: the erection of the scaffold and the deactivation of the old system. All this is shown in Figure 4.

FIGURE 4

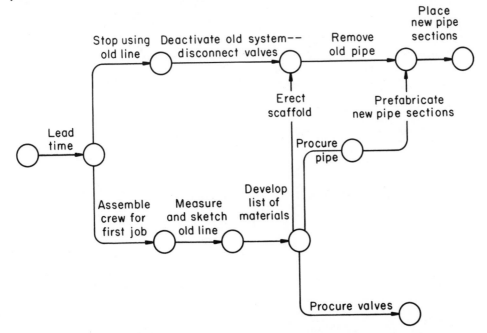

Let's return to the (procure valves) operation. After we have the valves, we can put them in place. But, before this can be done, the old system must be deactivated. This condition is shown in Figure 5.

FIGURE 5

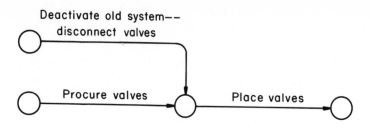

Referring to Figure 5, however, we see that the situation is not so simple since we wish to remove the old pipe after deactivating the old system. This, then, calls for a dummy, as indicated in Figure 6.

FIGURE 6

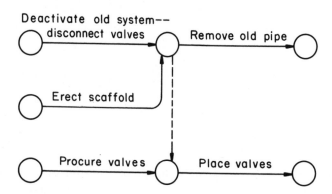

After the new pipe sections are in place, they can be welded together and then insulated. However, since the insulation will cover the area where the valves are placed, the pipe cannot be completely insulated until the valves are in place. Furthermore, the valves cannot be connected until the pipe sections are welded, and the insulation cannot be completed until the valves are completely connected. This situation is shown in Figure 7.

FIGURE 7

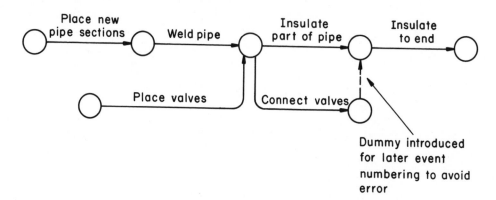

The whole project diagram to this stage, incorporating Figures 6 and 7, can be as illustrated as in Figure 8.

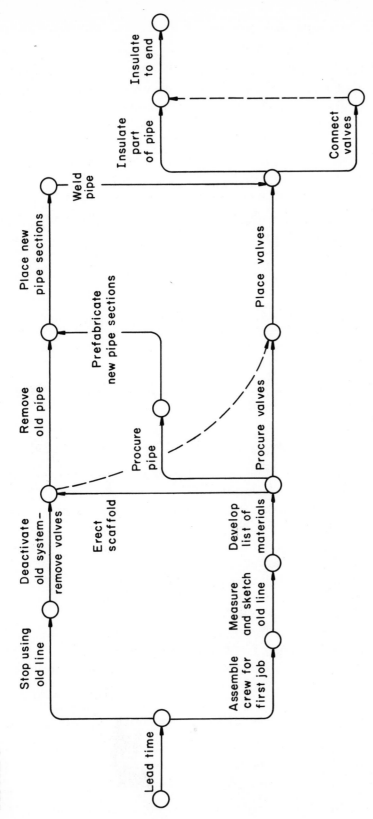

FIGURE 8

The only parts of the job still to be shown on the diagram are the pressure test, removal of the scaffold, and clean-up.

The scaffold should not be removed until after the pressure test, and the pressure test must be preceded by the final connection of the valves. Furthermore, it would be unwise to complete the insulation around the pipe joints and the valve joints until after the pressure test. This concept is shown in Figure 9.

FIGURE 9

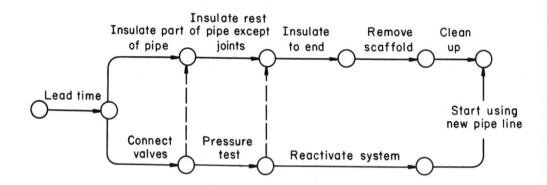

We have now completed the diagram for the project. Figure 10 shows the finished diagram, with numbered events.

Advantages

The advantages of arrow diagramming to create a simplified model of a project are apparent. The major ones are:

1. The diagram is a working model—it can be followed by anyone with very little explanation. Creating an arrow diagram is much more complex than reading one.
2. By means of a diagram, the entire project scope can be immediately, and visually, assimilated.
3. Problems are resolved, on paper, before they occur.
4. The chance of omission is substantially reduced.
5. Coordination of work and deliveries is achieved.
6. Work is planned in the order in which it *must* be done rather than in which it *could* be done.
7. For each job, all prerequisite work is always immediately evident.
8. Preparing an arrow diagram requires the cooperation of the people who will supervise or do the work. The result will be *their* plan— something they respect—rather than something imposed upon them.

There are no real disadvantages to arrow diagramming, although there *seem* to be three major ones: the amount of time, the effort, and the detail required. These objections will be considered in turn.

There is a commonly held belief that arrow-diagramming a project takes longer than more conventional approaches often centered about bar charts. This is quite true in the narrow, restricted sense of initial time only. It

FIGURE 10

Project 400. Final arrow diagram for chemical plant maintenance project:

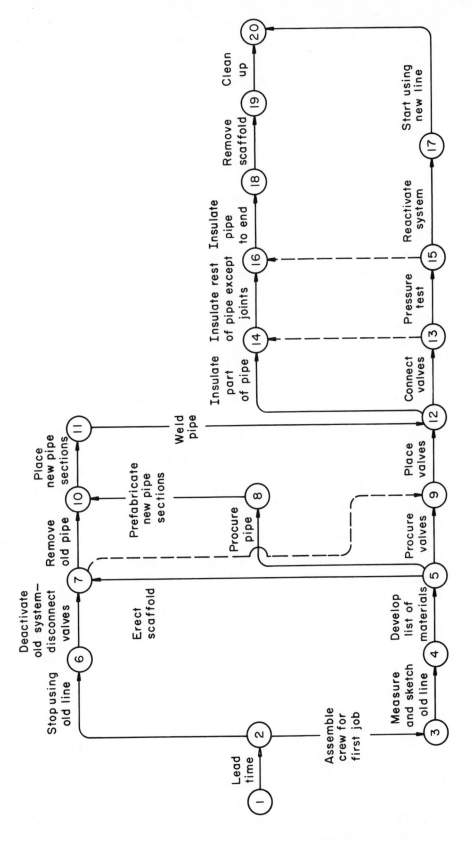

will take longer to prepare a *realistic* arrow diagram model of a project than to draw up a list of work and use the list to create a bar chart. Using a bar chart, however, requires a great deal more time during the life of the project than does an arrow diagram. This is due to many factors but mainly to these three: (1) with bar charts, problems are resolved *as* they occur, rather than *before* they occur; (2) the chance of omission is high; and (3) bar chart techniques are cumbersome as planning vehicles, and changes are difficult to make as the project unfolds. The overall effect is that bar charts, for the project as a whole, require *more* time than arrow diagrams. Hence, while it may take longer to prepare an arrow diagram than to draw a bar chart before the project starts, arrow diagrams will take *less* time for the project as a whole. And, of course, they are far more satisfactory.

Since the arrow diagram is to be a working model, it must be correct, and to make it so will require effort. While the basic rules of drawing arrow diagrams are so simple as to be almost trivial, the application of these rules to a real project is quite difficult. A great deal of thought is definitely required. However, this is not so much a disadvantage of this one technique as it is a fact of life. The greater the effort, the greater the return. The effort here is not in drawing arrows, but in deciding how to do the work. If no decision is reached, what is the point of even starting? The objection that preparing arrow diagrams requires effort is surely not valid.

The question of required detail is often raised. Planners too often claim that they have incomplete or inadequate knowledge. "How can an arrow diagram be drawn for the project of erecting a building before it is even designed?" they ask. This is an apparently valid objection; however, closer inspection will show it is invalid. If a building is going to be designed, then we will certainly have quite a bit of information concerning its size, layout, and so on. Furthermore, we have erected buildings before. Consequently, an arrow diagram of the logical steps required to erect the building *can* be prepared before the building is designed. As a matter of fact, the diagram should be prepared before all the design detail is complete. It is not difficult, afterward, to make any required additions or changes. In any case experience has shown that the number of changes which will most likely be required is not at all large.

Decision Diagrams

When we are setting out to invent something, the situation is only slightly different. We can create an arrow diagram—we have enough knowledge—but we come to a point where we could branch out in a number of different directions. That is, we must make a decision which will lead to the selection of just one line of work from among many possible approaches. The way to handle such situations is to diagram the alternatives.

To illustrate, let us consider a specific project. A pharmaceutical manufacturing company wishes to manufacture and sell a cure for a common cold.

The company realizes that after a preliminary study it may terminate all work. It further realizes that after this preliminary study it may find that the causes of the cold are known, in which case a cure has to be found before the necessary pills or injectables can be manufactured. If the causes are not known, however, then they must first be discovered before a cure can be developed. The final possibility is that both the cause and a possible cure will be known, and that the only requirement will be to begin manufacturing before entering the market.

These situations can be separately diagrammed as in Figure 11; or they can be shown all on one diagram, as in Figure 12. In Figure 12 the "diamond" indicates a decision to select one of the four possible paths, or alternative courses of action, after the initial study.

Since decision networks are highly specialized, space does not permit their complete delineation for handling decision points. The example does, however, indicate that it is possible to handle even the most nebulous situation in a network diagram.

Any objection, then, to using the arrow diagramming technique because of incomplete knowledge is invalid. We can, and should, always plan our work. If we can't, once again, how can we expect to start it?

In applying PERT/CPM to a project, arrow diagramming is the first but most important phase. If the sequence of activities (arrow diagram) is wrong, then the worth of any schedule produced is highly questionable. The need to prepare a completely accurate arrow diagram cannot be stressed too much.

In drawing arrow diagrams there are certain practical procedures which, while they are not "rules" in the full sense of the word, should be most helpful.

Rules of Good Practice

1. **Appearance.** It is best to use a "flow" approach with curved arrows rather than straight lines. The result is a diagram that "flows" to the right, rather than a disjointed entity. The comparison may be seen in Figure 13. The "cigar" or submarine shape is obviously easier to read.

2. **Long Arrows.** Quite often some job can start immediately but doesn't have to be finished until the end of the project. An example is job P in Figure 13.

In Project 401 there is no inconvenience because the resultant arrow diagram is small. On the other hand, if the project were large and complex, then the diagram might require a sheet of paper many feet long. If that is the case, what should be clear might be obscured by running arrows the entire length of the diagram.

FIGURE 11

Diagramming the four alternatives for the common cold project as four
separate diagrams:

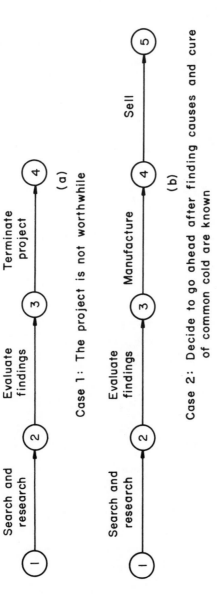

FIGURE 12

Diagramming the four alternatives for the common cold project in one diagram using a "decision box":

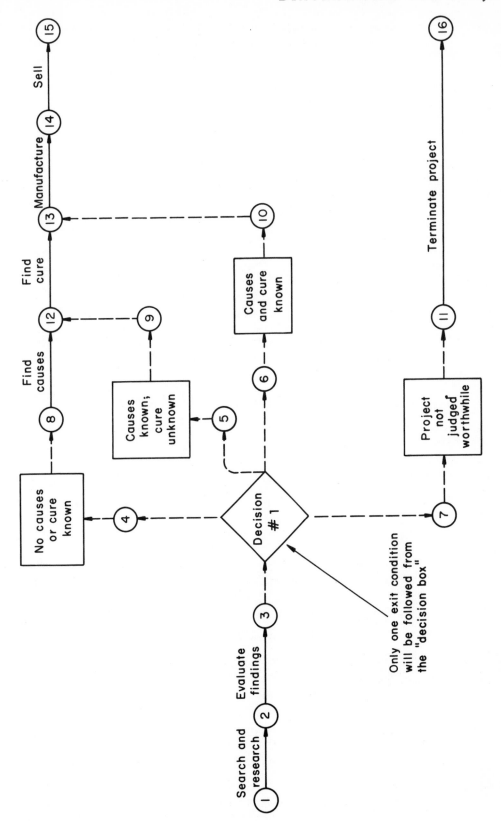

FIGURE 13   Project 401. The "cigar" shape shown in (a) is easier to read than the type of diagram shown in (b). Both are correct, but (a) is preferred:

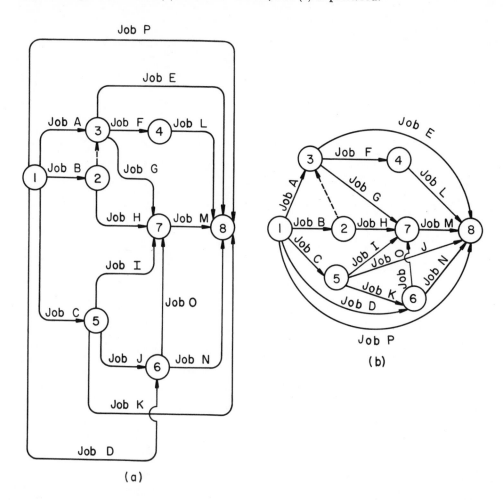

(a)

(b)

In order to avoid obscurity it is useful to draw a short arrow and to label the ending event immediately with some alphabetic designation. The true destination is also so labeled. Then, when the diagram is completed, the alphabetic designations can be replaced by the event numbers. An example is shown in Figure 14(a).

This procedure is useful in other cases as well. For instance, crossovers of many arrows can be eliminated, and this technique can be used to keep a large diagram on a short, but wide, sheet of paper. The main purpose of the short arrow is to provide an interim label for the sake of clarity. The interim label is replaced by the event number ultimately assigned.

FIGURE 14(a)   Jobs *A*, *B*, and *C* proceed to last event, and jobs *D* and *E* proceed to an event close to the end. Using the labels "a" and "b" clarifies the diagram. An alternative is shown in Figure 14(b). Both are equally acceptable and much better than drawing arrows 10 feet long to represent jobs *A*, *B*, *C*, *D*, and *E*:

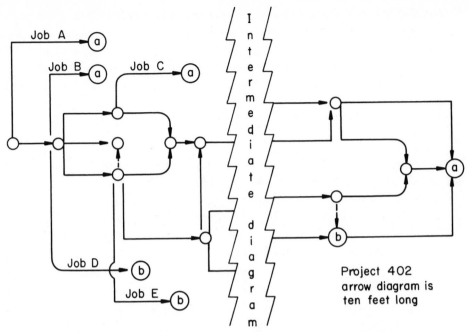

Since jobs *A*, *B*, and *C* are clustered and all lead to the last event (labeled "a"), they are brought to a single "pseudo event a," rather than to three separate ones. The same is true for jobs *D* and *E*, leading to "b"; this is useful only in the case of jobs like *A*, *B*, and *C* that "start" close together:

FIGURE 14(b)

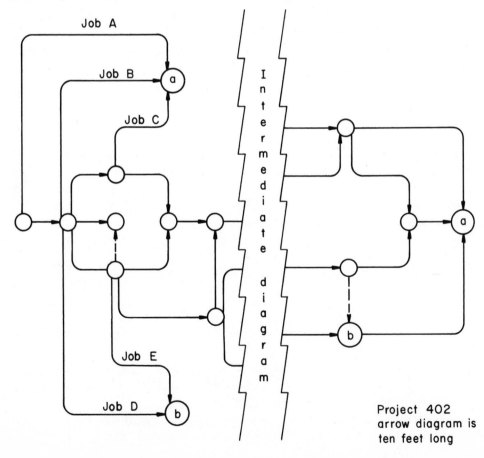

3. Numbering Events. While not mandatory it is nonetheless good practice to number events so that the number at the tail of an arrow is smaller than the number at the head, as we have seen. However, events need not be numbered consecutively, nor should the first event be numbered 1. In fact, it is wisest to leave gaps in the numbering sequence to take care of later additions. One useful idea is to number the diagram with only odd numbers. Then, if additions are made later, there is plenty of "room" for them as even numbers.

The best approach is to number the first event according to whether or not the diagram represents the whole project or only some one part of it. For example, if we have one diagram for the project of designing, building, and finishing the interior of a building, then we could (and should) start with 1; however, if there are three separate diagrams—one for design, one for erection, and one for interior finish—then it is better to use the numbers 1–300 for design, 301–600 for erection, and 601–900 for interior finish. Then the linkages between the separate diagrams will always satisfy the condition that the event number at the tail must be smaller than the number at the head.

These are, of course, only suggested guides. It is best to use common sense and select any approach that always clarifies what is intended.

Event Descriptions

PERT sometimes uses descriptions for events. The procedure is to establish milestones, or key points, and link them with arrows representing intermediate work. This may be illustrated by considering the pipeline construction project, No. 300, for which the key events, or milestones, are:

- Start of project.
- End of trenching.
- End of pipelaying.
- End of weld and test.
- End of project.
- Delivery of first batch of pipe.
- Delivery of last batch of pipe.

Summary

A diagram using only these milestones, or key events, will confuse those who must *do* the work, whereas for those who merely *observe* it the apparent simplicity seems ideal. However, to treat this subject properly it is necessary to refer to other aspects of the PERT/CPM techniques, and for that reason such a discussion is deferred until Chapter Seven.

1. Arrow diagrams are created to serve as a working model of the project.
2. Arrow diagrams express the logic of what *must* be done; hence they must be prepared in consultation with, and with the *active* assistance of, those who will do the work.
3. Arrow diagrams are an excellent means of displaying the logic of the work flow. Such a diagram is a master plan for the entire

project and, as such, can serve as a realistic and practical "working model."

Select any, or all, of the following projects. Draw the arrow diagrams.

1. You are the owner of a small contracting firm, and you are submitting a bid for the construction of a high-rise apartment house. Develop a logical plan for the erection of the apartments to be submitted along with the bid.

2. You and your wife have come to the conclusion that the house in which you are now living is too small and you must move to larger quarters. Develop a logical plan for finding yourself a larger home.

3. As director of manufacturing for an organization producing consumer goods, you are faced with moving a production line from its existing location to a new location on a different floor in the same building. Develop a plan for making the move with a minimum amount of lost production.

4. As president and chairman of the board of a large, diversified industrial organization, you have come to the conclusion that the general manager of one of your operating divisions must be replaced because of declining profit in that division. What is your plan for finding a new general manager?

5. As maintenance engineer for a large chemical process plant, you are faced with having to remove a very large valve during the next turn-around period. Develop a plan for replacing this valve.

6. You have recently been transferred from Stamford, Connecticut, to New York City. You and your wife are faced with finding a new apartment in New York. How would you go about it?

7. You are systems manager for a large engineering construction firm. Profits have been falling of late, and management has decided to install a system of cost control. You have been assigned the task of developing a plan for the accomplishment of this system. What is it?

8. You are the marketing vice president for an organization operating in the consumer goods area. Market research studies indicate the necessity of adding a new product to the current product line. Develop a plan to bring this new product to the market.

9. As the production engineer for the company in Question 8, how would you go about setting up the production line for the new product?

10. You are the office manager for a long-established downtown law firm that has decided to break with tradition and move to a new building uptown. Lay out a plan to make the move without disturbing the partners in the firm.

CHAPTER FOUR

Critical and Non-Critical Jobs—
Earliest Start

THE ULITIMATE OBJECTIVE OF APPLYING PERT/CPM to a project is to produce a schedule giving the calendar date on which each job will start. This presupposes that all the jobs cannot start simultaneously with the project, for then we would have a simple project with a simple solution. In actuality, the various tasks which make up a project have a number of different starting dates, only a few of which may be the same. The objective is to find these starting dates as part of the criteria required to produce a schedule.

In finding the starting time for an activity, we sometimes discover that there is a variation in possible starting time. Some jobs could start on any date during a certain range in time and not affect the completion date for the project as a whole. For instance, if we are building a row of homes on a new street created for a housing development, then at some time we have to erect a street sign. Now this job, which is quite short, can be done at any time. It, then, has a variation in starting time.

Other jobs can have no variation in starting time. In the housing development referred to, no construction work whatsoever can proceed until we prepare the site. Hence, delaying this preparation job beyond its earliest starting date will obviously delay the whole project.

Total Float

Any job that has no variation in starting time is critical, and a job with a possible variation in starting time is non-critical. The difference between the earliest starting time and the latest starting time of a job, therefore, is a measure of criticality. If the difference is zero, the job is critical; if it is not zero, the job is not critical. This difference is called "total float," and it is a very important quantity in any scheduling procedure. The use of total float in scheduling will be considered later.

The scheduling criteria, then, to be derived from the plan are two:

1. The earliest possible starting time for each activity.
2. The variation in starting time (difference between earliest possible and latest possible starts), called total float, which may be zero.

To find the earliest starting time for each activity, three things are required:

Earliest Starting Date of Each Activity

1. The starting date of the project.
2. The sequential relationship of all jobs in the project to the jobs that start at the beginning of the project.
3. The duration of each job in the project.

We shall take these three requirements in order.

The project starting date is something that need not be known to apply the principles of PERT/CPM. Quite obviously, the date on which work will start is a very important fact, but if we say that the starting date may be represented as "zero time" and if we develop numbers relative to this base, then everything is fully known when we establish the calendar value of zero time. If we have a job that will start at time 10 (ten days after zero time), we know that 10 represents September 25th if zero time is September 15th. This artifice of specifying zero time for the start of the project has two advantages: (1) It does not delay planning and scheduling procedures if the starting date is not known, and (2) it is more convenient to work with relative time numbers like 0 or 10 than with calendar dates. Of these two advantages the latter is the more important. Furthermore, there is no difficulty whatever in attaching calendar dates afterward, and it is actually more convenient if the starting date is changed.

Sequence and Duration

The sequential relationships of all the jobs are completely determined through logic and displayed for ready visual assimilation on an arrow diagram network. The duration (or measure of time) is estimated according to the selected method of performance.

The overall problem of estimating the duration and cost of an activity, according to the method of performance selected, will be considered in depth in Volume 2, *Applied Operational Planning*, with particular attention to the use of probability and the handling of contingencies. For the present we assume that the number being used as a time measure of duration is a valid estimate, and we develop and establish certain arithmetic procedures which use such durations to find the earliest starting times for all jobs in the project. With a knowledge of earliest start and of duration the earliest finish can be found by simple addition.

**Earliest
Activity Start**

The best way to illustrate the development of the rules for finding the earliest activity starting time is by analogy.

Consider two trains. Train 1 starts out from City *A* and Train 2 starts out from City *B* (see Figure 1). These trains will both travel to City *C*, along different tracks, with a different running time. At City *C*, they will be hooked together and proceed to the final destination, City *D*. In Figure 1 the earliest possible time to start the hook-up procedure is 3 P.M. The significant fact here is that the hook-up depends on the presence of *both* trains. While Train 2 from City *B* arrives at 2 P.M., hook-up must necessarily be delayed until Train 1 arrives at 3 P.M.

FIGURE 1 Time relationships of train analogy:

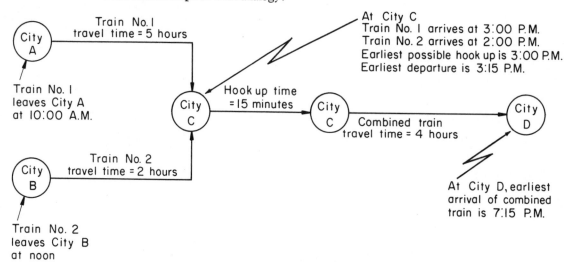

In order to simplify the detail of this diagrammatic relationship, various standards of nomenclature can be introduced, as in Figure 2.

FIGURE 2 Duration attached to bottom of arrow:

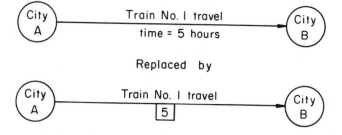

In this diagram we have attached the duration to the underside of the horizontal arrow. If the arrow were vertical, we would attach the duration to its right side. The one requirement is to use the same standard for all time units. In this case we must select minutes or hours. The alternatives are shown in Figures 3(a) and 3(b).

FIGURE 3(a)

Hours as standard:

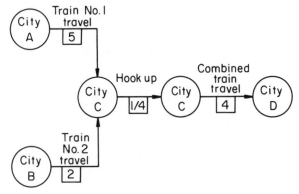

FIGURE 3(b)

Minutes as standard:

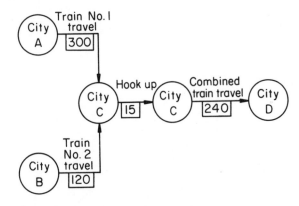

Consider the information at each city. We have:

1. City identification.
2. Arrival time.
3. Departure time (earliest possible or scheduled).

Labeling and Other Conventions

In any complicated network we would certainly (and rapidly) clutter up the diagrammatic representation by scattering references and statements all over it. A simple expedient is to select a time base of zero and a standard to measure differences and to work in time units relative to these standards. If we select midnight as zero time and hours as the standard time unit, then 10 A.M. becomes 10; noon, 12; 3 P.M., 15; 3:15 P.M., 15¼; and 7:30 P.M., 19½. Furthermore, in order to call attention to the fact that a number refers to the earliest starting time, we can either represent it in a certain way (using a square box) or always put it in a certain place, as in Figures 4(a) and 4(b).

Showing earliest start by a standard; confusion could arise in a complex network as to which city a specific earliest start time belongs:

FIGURE 4(a)

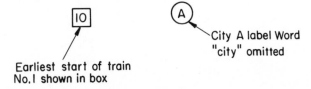

Earliest start of train No.1 shown in box

City A label Word "city" omitted

FIGURE 4(b)   Showing earliest start as a standard, but, more importantly, in a fixed location, directly linked to the city to avoid confusion as to which city a standard time belongs:

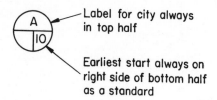

By means of the conventions listed below, Figure 1 is simplified to the display shown in Figure 5:

- Time zero is midnight.
- Standard time units are hours.
- The duration is attached to the arrow representing train travel or train hook-up.
- Earliest starting time is placed in the right-hand side of the lower half of the city label.

FIGURE 5   Simplified version of train situation using pre-established conventions:

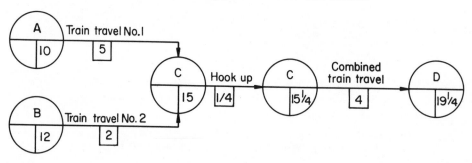

Rules for Finding Earliest Activity Starts

Using the conventions we have established, we can consider the simple project in Figure 6. Note that, for clarity, alphabetic descriptions have been omitted and jobs will be described by their event labels.

FIGURE 6   Project 501. To be used to develop rules of earliest activity starting times; durations are in standard time units—say, days—and project starts at time zero. Note: There can be no duplication of event labels:

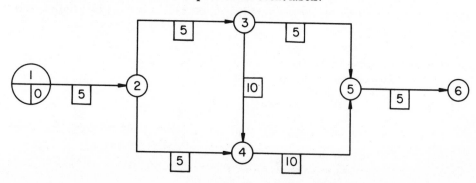

In this case, city labels are replaced by event labels. Hence, there can be no label duplication (as in the case of two labels in Figure 5 for City C) since we are dealing with events as junctions of arrows rather than with geographical locations.

According to our previously established convention for basing all project times relative to zero time, we know that all activities starting at the first event, or at the start of the project, have an earliest start of zero. In that case, job (1,2) has an earliest starting time of zero, as shown in Figure 6. From this starting point the objective is to proceed and find the earliest starting times of all the other activities. The first rule, and a cardinal one, is to proceed from each event to the next in order (from event 1, to event 2, to event 3, to event 4, and so on to the last event). The reason will be apparent later. Proceeding in this manner, the immediate questions are: What is the starting time of job (2,3)? Or what is the starting time of job (2,4)? Which do we tackle first, or are the answers to both questions identical?

From the rules of arrow diagramming we know that jobs (2,3) and (2,4) are concurrent in the sense that both can be done at any time following the completion of job (1,2). Hence, the earliest starting times for jobs (2,3) and (2,4) are identical to the earliest time when job (1,2) can be completed. In this case, since job (1,2) has a duration of 5, its earliest finish is 5 (earliest start of 0 plus a duration of 5), and the earliest start for jobs (2,3) and (2,4) is 5. This is shown in Figure 7.

As a matter of fact, since job (1,2) is the only one that ends at event 2, then 5 would be the earliest starting time for all the jobs that started at event 2. As a result, although we are interested in the starting time of each and every specific activity, we have found that we actually develop a single number at each event that represents the earliest starting time for *all* activities out of that event. What we now have at each event is a number representing the earliest starting time of all the activities originating there.

FIGURE 7

Earliest start out of event 2:

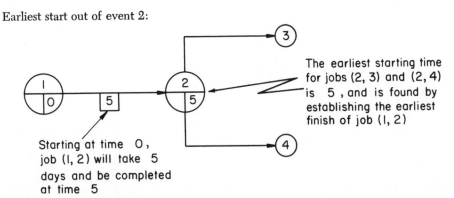

Starting at time 0, job (1, 2) will take 5 days and be completed at time 5

The earliest starting time for jobs (2, 3) and (2, 4) is 5, and is found by establishing the earliest finish of job (1, 2)

The Quantity E

The preceding discussion implies that the earliest activity start times are associated with the event on whose completion they depend. A name is obviously more convenient than such unwieldy phraseology as "the earliest starting times of all the jobs starting from event 2." Historically, the term used has been "earliest event time" at event 2. This term has resulted in some confusion, because an "event time," as such, is fictitious. An event is a point in time which consumes no time in its occurrence. Activities, on the other hand, consume time, start at some event, and end at another event. To have a term like "event time" could easily confuse the situation regarding activity time (or duration) and activity start and finish times. For that reason the historic term "earliest event time" is not satisfactory.

Another term which could be used is "earliest event number." This phrase is better since it does not introduce a potentially confusing reference to time. However, since we really want some short and simple reference to denote the earliest possible start time for all activities at an event, the simplest thing to do is to let E represent this phrase. Then, through a subscript representing the event, the meaning is perfectly clear and the quantity is completely defined.

If we adopt this approach, the earliest starting time for all jobs starting at event 2 is represented by the single symbol, E_2. In our example, $E_2 =$ 5. Hence, the earliest start of job (2,3) = 5, and the earliest start of job (2,4) = 5. The problem, then, of finding the earliest start time for each activity in a project is reduced to finding the value of E at each event, beginning at the first event, and proceeding in order (or sequence) to the last event.

Using this symbolism and notation, we proceed to event 3, where we wish to find E_3, or the earliest starting time of all jobs out of event 3: jobs (3,4) and (3,5) in this case. The completion of all work leading to event 3 depends upon the completion of job (2,3). With an earliest start of 5 and a duration of 5 the earliest finish of job (2,3) is 10. No other jobs lead into event 3; hence, no other requirements must be met before the jobs out of event 3 can start. Thus the earliest start of jobs (3,4) and (3,5) is 10; that is, $E_3 = 10$. In retrospect, the procedure was as follows:

$$\text{Earliest finish job } (2,3) = E_2 + \text{duration of job } (2,3)$$
$$= 5 + 5$$
$$= 10$$
$$= E_3$$

The situation to this point is shown in Figure 8.

FIGURE 8   Calculation of E up to event 3:

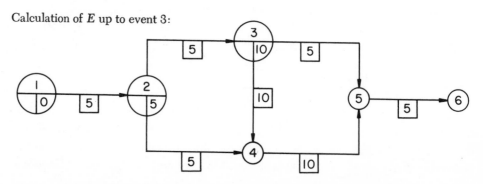

The next step is to find E_4. Here the situation is different from that encountered at events 2 and 3: Before job (4,5) can start, *both* jobs (2,4) *and* (3,4) must be completed. In this case:

$$\text{Earliest finish of job } (2,4) = E_2 + \text{duration of job } (2,4)$$
$$= 5 + 5$$
$$= 10$$

And:

$$\text{Earliest finish of job } (3,4) = E_3 + \text{duration of job } (3,4)$$
$$= 10 + 10$$
$$= 20$$

The situation at event 4 is similar to that at City C in the train analogy. Train 2 arrived an hour before Train 1. Obviously, however, the hook-up of the two trains was delayed until both trains arrived. That is, *the hook-up was delayed until the latest arrival.* Similarly, at event 4 the earliest start of job (4,5) is 20, and not 10, since *both* preceding jobs must be completed. While job (2,4) does end at 10, we must still await the completion of job (3,4) before we can start job (4,5). As a matter of fact, job (2,4) could end at the same time that job (3,4) starts, but we still must wait till job (3,4) ends before starting (4,5).

Another way of saying the same thing is this: The earliest starting time of all the jobs starting at any event equals the largest value of the earliest finish times of all the jobs ending at that event. In terms of E:

$$E_{\substack{\text{current} \\ \text{event}}} = \text{largest value of earliest finishes at current event}$$

In the case of event 4:

$$E_4 = \text{larger value of} \begin{Bmatrix} \text{earliest finish job } (2,4) \\ \text{earliest finish job } (3,4) \end{Bmatrix}$$
$$= \text{larger value of} \begin{Bmatrix} 10 \\ 20 \end{Bmatrix}$$
$$= 20$$

This situation is depicted in Figures 9 and 10.

In Figure 9 vertical lines are drawn to represent a time scale. The first day extends from time 0 to time 1, the second day from time 1 to time 2, and so on. This principle is best understood by considering the way we compute age. At birth we have no age. After our first year of life, we have a first birthday, achieve an age of 1, and begin our second year of life. This is the same procedure as using the vertical time scale approach shown in Figure 9.

FIGURE 9   Visual determination of $E_4 = 20$:

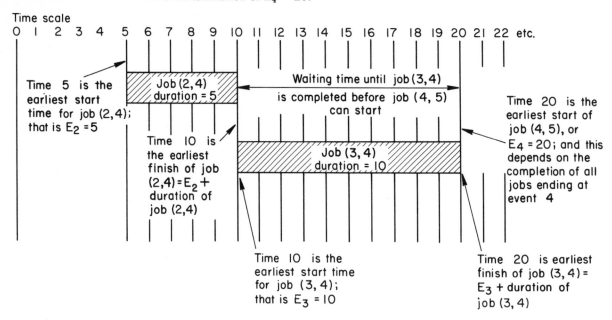

FIGURE 10   Values of E up to event 4:

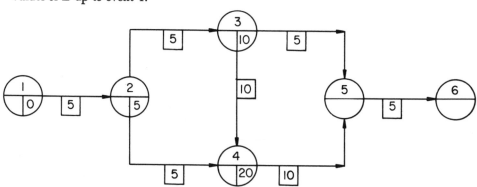

Before proceeding to calculate E_5, it will be well to introduce some further abbreviations that will simplify the phraseology. We let—

E.F. = earliest finish
D   = duration

Now, to refer to a specific job—say, job (2,4)—we use subscript notation as follows:

$D_{(2,4)}$ = duration of job (2,4)
$E.F._{(2,4)}$ = earliest finish of job (2,4)

and so on. Using this notation, the previous calculation for E_4 can be represented as—

$$E = larger \begin{Bmatrix} E.F._{(2,4)} \\ E.F._{(3,4)} \end{Bmatrix}$$

$$\begin{aligned} \text{E.F.}_{(2,4)} &= E_2 + D_{(2,4)} \\ &= 5 + 5 \\ &= 10 \end{aligned}$$

and—

$$\begin{aligned} \text{E.F.}_{(3,4)} &= E_3 + D_{(3,4)} \\ &= 10 + 10 \\ &= 20 \end{aligned}$$

Then—

$$\begin{aligned} E_4 &= \text{larger} \begin{Bmatrix} 10 \\ 20 \end{Bmatrix} \\ &= 20 \end{aligned}$$

We thus proceed to event 5. The situation is that jobs $(3,5)$ and $(4,5)$ end at event 5. Now— **Earliest Start at Event 5**

$$\begin{aligned} \text{E.F.}_{(3,5)} &= E_3 + D_{(3,5)} \\ &= 10 + 5 \\ &= 15 \end{aligned}$$

and—

$$\begin{aligned} \text{E.F.}_{(4,5)} &= E_4 + D_{(4,5)} \\ &= 20 + 10 \\ &= 30 \end{aligned}$$

Hence—

$$\begin{aligned} E_5 &= \text{larger} \begin{Bmatrix} \text{E.F.}_{(3,5)} \\ \text{E.F.}_{(4,5)} \end{Bmatrix} \\ &= \text{larger} \begin{Bmatrix} 15 \\ 30 \end{Bmatrix} \\ &= 30 \end{aligned}$$

In real life, relations such as these are not written down. A more practical procedure is as follows: **Practical Procedure**

Step 1: At each event, starting at the first and using the value of E at that event, find the earliest finish of all the jobs starting at that event. Mark these values lightly close to the head of the respective arrow for each. Proceed to the next event.

Step 2: Select the largest value of the earliest finish for all the jobs that end at the event. Place this value in the appropriate location in the event label. Erase the working values marked on the diagram. Then, at that event, perform Step 1, and so on.

This procedure is illustrated in Figures 11 to 15.

FIGURE 11 Procedure at event 1:

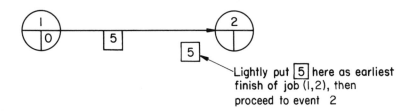

Lightly put ⬜5 here as earliest finish of job (1,2), then proceed to event 2

FIGURE 12 Procedure at event 2:

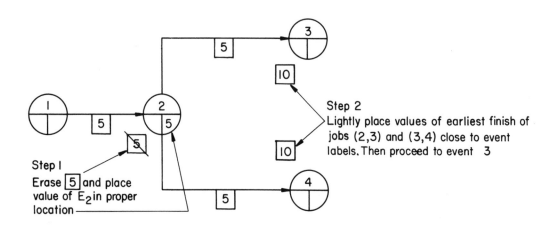

Step 1
Erase ⬜5 and place value of E_2 in proper location

Step 2
Lightly place values of earliest finish of jobs (2,3) and (3,4) close to event labels. Then proceed to event 3

FIGURE 13 Procedure at event 3:

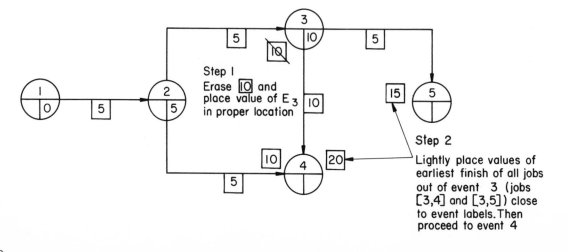

Step 1
Erase ⬜10 and place value of E_3 in proper location

Step 2
Lightly place values of earliest finish of all jobs out of event 3 (jobs [3,4] and [3,5]) close to event labels. Then proceed to event 4

Procedure at event 4:   **FIGURE 14**

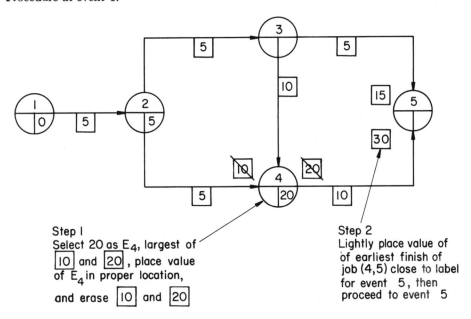

Step I
Select 20 as E₄, largest of
10 and 20 , place value
of E_4 in proper location,
and erase 10 and 20

Step 2
Lightly place value of
of earliest finish of
job (4,5) close to label
for event 5, then
proceed to event 5

Procedure at event 5:   **FIGURE 15**

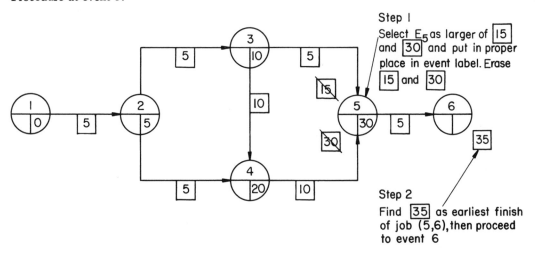

Step I
Select E_5 as larger of 15
and 30 and put in proper
place in event label. Erase
15 and 30

Step 2
Find 35 as earliest finish
of job (5,6), then proceed
to event 6

This step-by-step procedure guarantees accuracy and speed. Visual scanning is *not* recommended, except in obvious cases like selecting E_2, E_3, and E_6.

With regard to event 6, the value of 35 is obvious. By definition, E_6 is the earliest start of jobs out of event 6. But there are none, since event 6 is the last event in the arrow diagram, marking the end of the project. From the manner in which E is calculated (that is, as the largest value of the earliest activity finishes to the event), it is quite obvious that the value of E for the last event is the earliest possible project completion.* And this is a very useful piece of information, to say the least.

The Last Event

*This presupposes no expediting, logic refinement, and so on—all topics which will be covered in Volume 2, *Applied Operational Planning*. On the basis of the arrow diagram and the durations specified, $E_{\text{latest event}}$ is the project duration.

Dummies

Handling dummies in finding E is no problem whatsoever. Dummies are handled exactly like real activities by taking a duration of zero. For diagrammatic simplicity, however, the 0 is not attached to the dummy as its duration; the obvious is *always* omitted.

Four cases of finding values for E where dummies exist are shown in Figures 16(a), (b), (c), and (d).

FIGURE 16

Finding E where dummies exist:

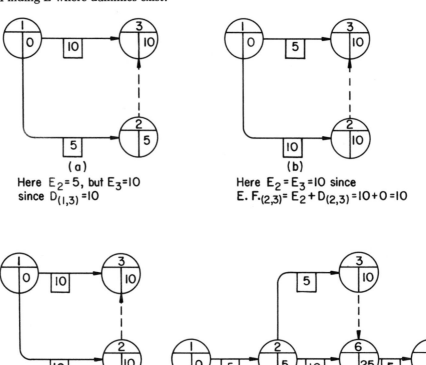

(a)

Here $E_2 = 5$, but $E_3 = 10$
since $D_{(1,3)} = 10$

(b)

Here $E_2 = E_3 = 10$ since
E. F.$_{(2,3)} = E_2 + D_{(2,3)} = 10 + 0 = 10$

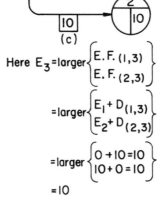

(c)

Here $E_3 = $ larger $\left\{ \begin{array}{l} \text{E. F. } (1,3) \\ \text{E. F. } (2,3) \end{array} \right\}$

$= $ larger $\left\{ \begin{array}{l} E_1 + D_{(1,3)} \\ E_2 + D_{(2,3)} \end{array} \right\}$

$= $ larger $\left\{ \begin{array}{l} 0 + 10 = 10 \\ 10 + 0 = 10 \end{array} \right\}$

$= 10$

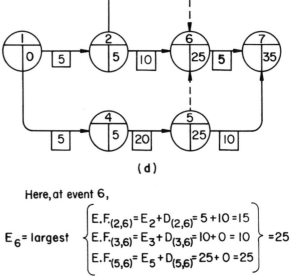

(d)

Here, at event 6,

$E_6 = $ largest $\left\{ \begin{array}{l} \text{E.F.}_{(2,6)} = E_2 + D_{(2,6)} = 5 + 10 = 15 \\ \text{E.F.}_{(3,6)} = E_3 + D_{(3,6)} = 10 + 0 = 10 \\ \text{E.F.}_{(5,6)} = E_5 + D_{(5,6)} = 25 + 0 = 25 \end{array} \right\} = 25$

Summary

The following rules apply for finding the earliest start of each activity in a project.

1. The earliest starts for all activities stemming from an event are represented by the symbol E, and a subscript specifies the event in question; for instance, jobs out of event 2 have an earliest start equal to E_2.

2. Values for E are found at events by proceeding in sequential order by event number, no matter how the diagram is numbered. (Never be tempted to "break" sequence for an "easy" case.)

3. $E_{\substack{\text{current} \\ \text{event}}} = \text{largest} \left\{ \begin{array}{l} \text{E.F. of all activities} \\ \text{ending at current event} \\ \text{under study} \end{array} \right\}$

This formula means that, at any event, the earliest starting time of commencing activities depends on the completion of *all* activities flowing into the event, and thus the start time numerically equals the largest value of earliest finish date for the activities ending at that event.

4. A simplified procedure for finding E is as follows. At each event, starting at the first event, find the earliest finish of all jobs starting out of the event, marking the answers *lightly*, close to the label for the ending event of each job. Then proceed to the next event, select the largest value of the finish times (take the largest number), enter it in the proper location in the event label, erase the working numbers, find the earliest finish for all the jobs out of the event, and so on.

5. $E_{\text{last event}} = $ earliest finish of entire project.

6. Dummies are handled just like real jobs with a zero duration.

Find E at each event in the following arrow diagrams:

Exercises

1. Project 502:

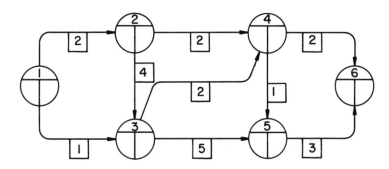

2. Project 503:

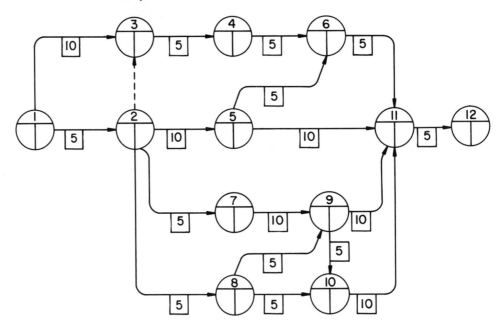

3. Project 504:

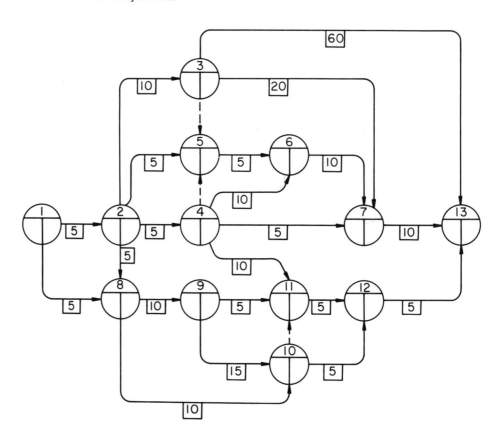

4. Project 300: Pipeline construction project:

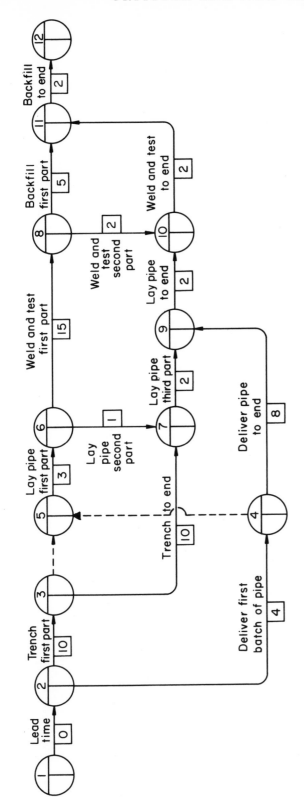

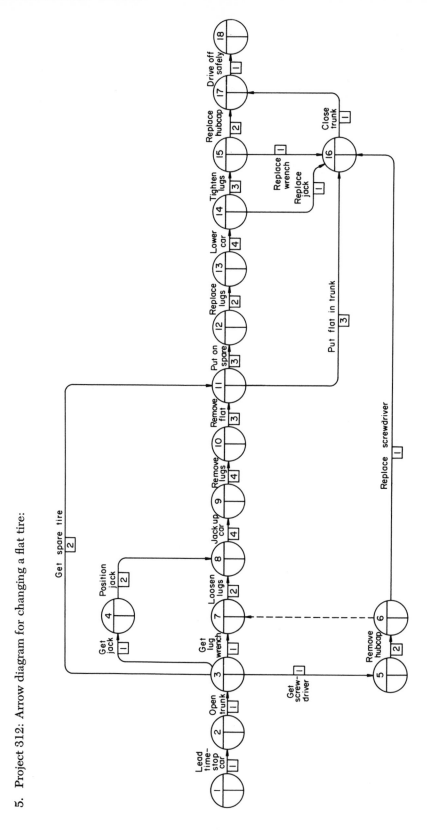

5. Project 312: Arrow diagram for changing a flat tire:

6. Project 400: Chemical plant maintenance project:

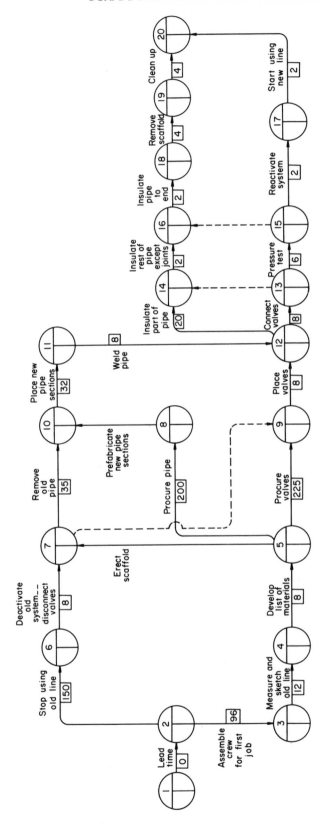

Solutions

1. Project 502:

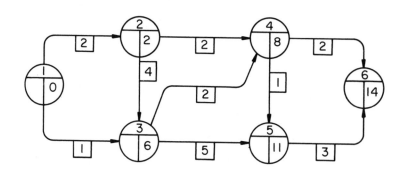

2. Project 503:

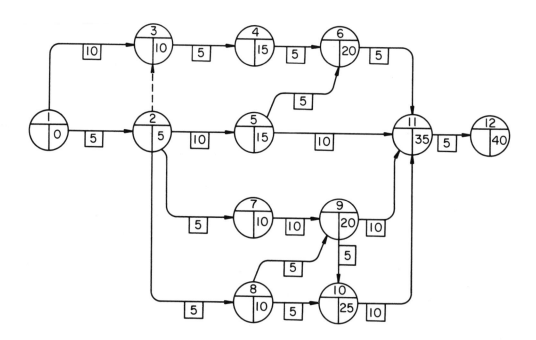

3. Project 504:

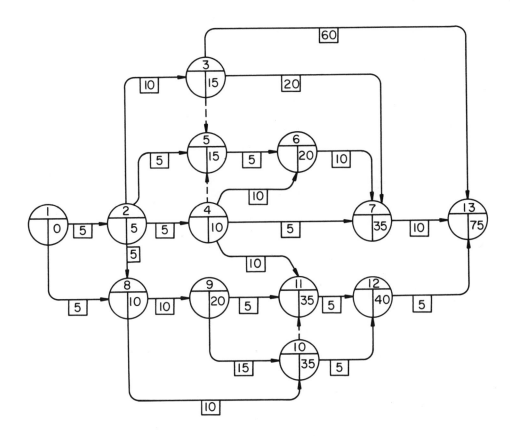

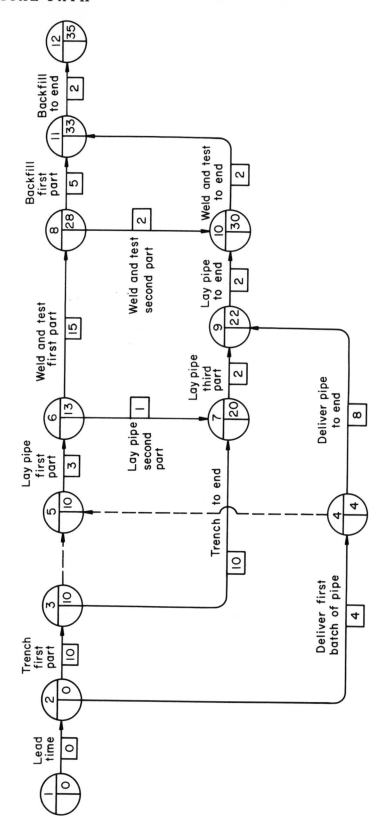

4. Project 300: Pipeline construction project:

5. Project 312: Arrow diagram for changing a flat tire:

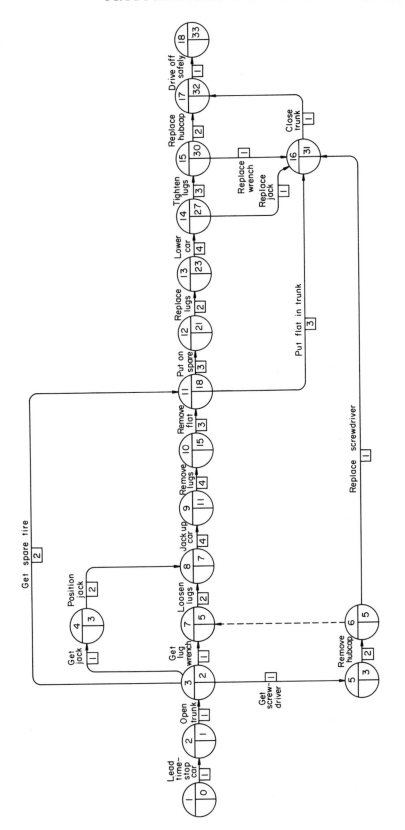

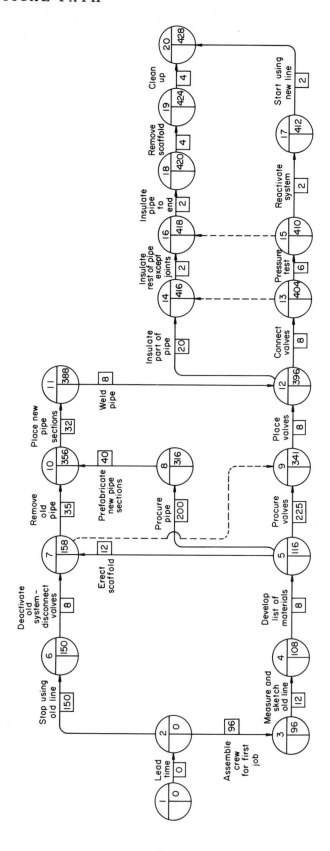

6. Project 400: Chemical plant maintenance project:

CHAPTER FIVE

Critical and Non-Critical Jobs— Latest Start

AFTER THE EARLIEST ACTIVITY starting time has been determined, the next step is to establish the criticality of each job; that is, to determine whether a variation in starting time is possible. The variation in starting time, it will be remembered, is called "total float," and any job with a total float of zero is critical. Any connected chain of critical jobs from the first to the last event is called the "critical path."

In order to find the total float of any job two items of information are required: (1) the earliest starting time and (2) the latest starting time. The earliest starting time for each job is determined by finding E at each event.

In the absence of any other direct procedure the latest starting time can be found by subtracting the activity duration from the latest possible finish. Hence, the objective is to find the latest finish times of each activity in the project.

As before, we shall use our train analogy to help develop rules for determining the latest finish times for the activities of a project. Consider the case illustrated in Figure 1.

Train Analogy

Our problem here is to arrange for arrival of the combined train at City D no later than 7:15 P.M. Since the travel time from City C to City D is four hours, the latest possible finish of the hook-up function is 3:15 P.M. This is found by subtracting the travel time of four hours from the latest possible arrival time of 7:15 P.M.

FIGURE 1

Train example with time units in hours:

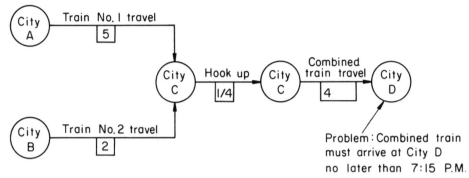

Similarly, the latest possible arrival of both trains at City C is 3 P.M. This is found by subtracting the duration of the hook-up procedure, 15 minutes, from the latest possible end of the hook-up function, 3:15 P.M.

With a latest arrival of both trains at City C of 3 P.M., we can find the conditions on Train 1's arrival at City A and on Train 2's arrival at City B by continuing to move backward. Train 1 takes five hours to travel from City A to City C, and its latest possible arrival at City C is 3 P.M. Consequently, all the work required to get Train 1 out of City A must be completed by no later than 10 A.M. Similarly, all the work necessary to get Train 2 moving out of City B must be completed by 1 P.M. The final results of this procedure are shown in Figure 2.

FIGURE 2

Display of all requirements on functions at Cities A, B, and C to meet the requirements that the combined train must arrive at City D no later than 7:15 P.M.:

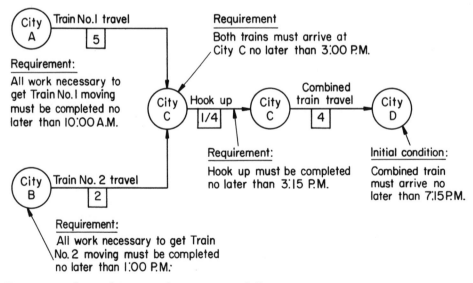

To recapitulate, the procedure was as follows:

    1. A completion condition was imposed at City D, the final destination—a latest possible arrival of 7:15 P.M. was set.

2. At City C the latest completion for the hook-up function, 3:15 P.M., was found by subtracting the travel time from City C to City D (four hours) from the initially set condition of a latest arrival at City D of 7:15 P.M. This was equivalent to saying that the latest starting time for the train out of City C is 3:15 P.M.

3. With the imposed condition of having the hook-up work at City C completed no later than 3:15 P.M., we found that both Trains 1 and 2 had to be at City C no later than 3 P.M. This we did by subtracting the required time of 15 minutes for the hook-up function from the required latest completion. Hence, in addition to establishing a latest arrival on Trains 1 and 2, we determined a latest starting time for the hook-up function.

4. Moving backward, we found that all work required to get Train 1 moving had to be completed by 10 A.M., which was equivalent to saying that Train 1 had a latest start of 10 A.M.

5. In the same fashion, we discovered that Train 2 must leave City B no later than 1 P.M.

This whole procedure may be summarized as follows: A total completion condition was set at the final destination (7:15 P.M. at City D). Conditions concerning the latest completion and latest start at each city for each function were found by moving backward through the network, subtracting the required time from previously established completion conditions (whether the initial one or a developed one; for instance, the condition that both trains had to arrive at City C no later than 3 P.M. led to the conditions at City A and City B).

FIGURE 3

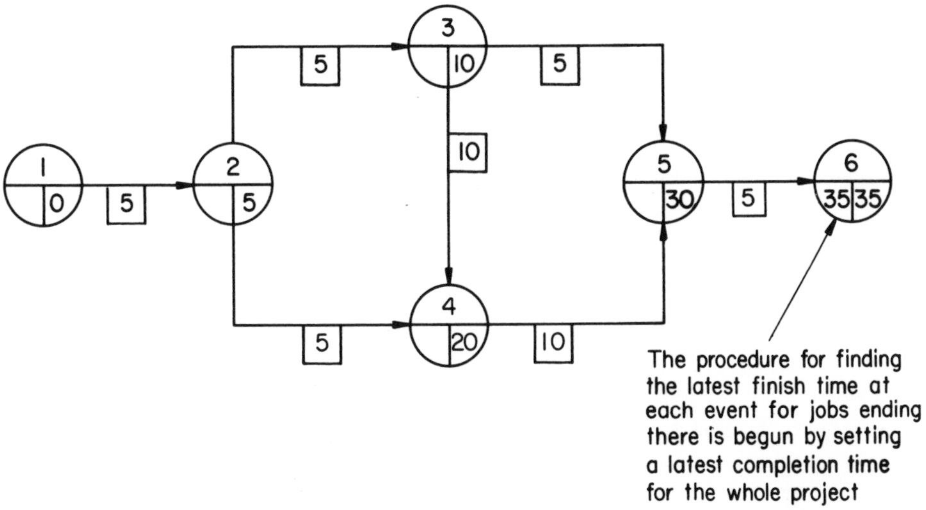

The procedure for finding the latest finish time at each event for jobs ending there is begun by setting a latest completion time for the whole project

The project shown in Figure 3 is the same one we used to determine the procedures for finding the earliest activity start times. We found that the calculation procedure for E led to $E_6 = 35$; that is, the earliest finish time

Latest Activity Finish Times

for the project is 35 time units, or days, since days were selected as the standard time unit.

If the project can be completed in 35 days, then there is no point in taking longer than 35 days. For that reason, selecting the initial condition on the project of a latest possible completion of 35 is both reasonable and sensible. While any condition whatsoever could be imposed as the final project completion time, selecting a duration longer than necessary would, obviously, not be realistic.

On the other hand, there are many occasions when a completion date short of the earliest finish for the project is desired or required—which, in our example, is equivalent to imposing a latest completion at event 6 of less than 35. For the present such cases will be ignored. In the companion volume, *Applied Operational Planning*, the method of satisfying an imposed completion time, not only at the end of the project but also at any point within it, will be considered in detail.

For the present, it seems both sensible and realistic to say that the latest possible finish for the project is the same as the earliest possible finish. This will be the first rule in finding the latest activity finish times. Just as the earlier discussion on earliest start times led to the selection of the symbol E, the symbol L^* will represent the latest finish times of all the activities which end at some event, and, once again, subscripts will be used to denote the actual event in question. Applying this notation, then, to Figure 3, we arrive at the following:

- The latest finish of job (5,6) is L_6.
- The latest finish of jobs (3,5) and (4,5) is L_5.
- The latest finish of jobs (2,4) and (3,4) is L_4.
- The latest finish of job (2,3) is L_3.
- The latest finish of job (1,2) is L_2.

The problem is to establish the manner in which L is found at each event. The first rule has already been established:

$L_{\text{last event}} = E_{\text{last event}}$. In this case, $L_6 = E_6 = 35$

In addition, as before, a symbol or location will be selected to represent the value of L at each event. It formerly was standard procedure to place a number in a circle close to the event label, as in Figure 4(a). As shown in Figure 4(b), however, and as used in Figure 3, the standard location can most usefully be inside the event label. While circles and squares could be used inside the event label, there is no need for either; the meaning of the number will depend solely on its location. (See Figure 5).

---

* The term "latest event time" has been historically used in the literature for L. However, just as with E, using the phrase "event time" could be misleading. For that reason the historic term "latest event time" is not recommended and is not used in this book.

Possible conventions for locating E and L values on an arrow diagram:

FIGURE 4

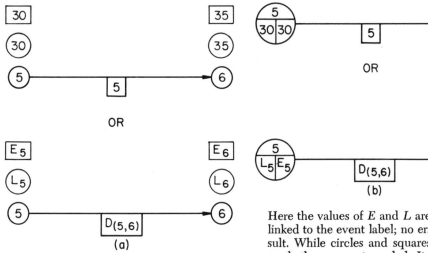

(a)

(b)

Here squares and circles close to event labels are used for E and L. This is good, but it could introduce confusion in complex networks as to exactly which event a circle or box belongs. That is, while it is good, it is not completely satisfactory.

Here the values of E and L are definitely linked to the event label; no error can result. While circles and squares could be used, they are not needed. It should be remembered that jobs come in at the left and have a latest finish of L; hence the value of L is at the bottom left hand. Jobs going out of an event go out to the right with an earliest start equal to E; the value of E is found at the bottom right.

Conventions for E and L adopted. Note that circles and squares are not used inside the event labels:

FIGURE 5

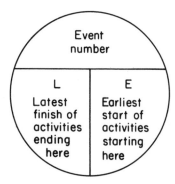

Next, proceed backward in sequence to event 4. Hence—

$$L_4 = L_5 - D_{(4,5)}$$
$$= 30 - 10$$
$$= 20 .$$

Furthermore—

Latest start of job $(4,5) = 20$.

This situation may be seen in Figure 6.

FIGURE 6

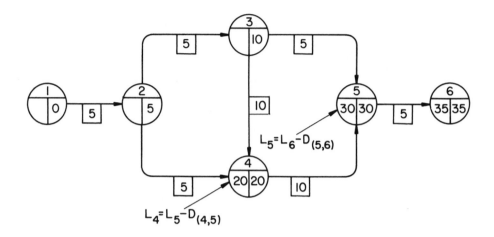

Note that an abbreviation will be used, as before:

L.F.   = latest finish
L.S.   = latest start
L.F.$_{(4,5)}$ = latest finish of job $(4,5)$
L.S.$_{(4,5)}$ = latest start of job $(4,5)$

and so on.

Using this notation, consider the situation at event 3. At this point—

Since L_5 $=$ 30, then L.F.$_{(3,5)} = 30$
But $D_{(3,5)}$ $=$ 5
Then L.S.$_{(3,5)}$ $=$ 25
Also L_4 $=$ 20
And $D_{(3,4)}$ $=$ 10
Then L.S.$_{(3,4)}$ $=$ 10

What, then, is L_3? Is L_3 equal to 10 or 25? Suppose that L_3 equals 25, the larger of the two possible answers. This means that job $(2,3)$ can end as late as time 25, which in turn means that job $(3,4)$ cannot start until time 25. But we have just found that the latest possible start for job $(3,4)$ is 10 if the condition that the whole project is to be completed no later than time 35 is to be met. Hence, L_3 *is not equal to 25*. This is illustrated in Figure 7.

Consequently, L_3 is equal to 10, the smaller of the two possible answers at event 3. Actually, this is quite logical. The latest finish into an event *must* equal the smallest of the latest starts out of the event. Otherwise, if a preceding job finishes later than the latest start of a succeeding job, obviously the latest start condition is violated, and this "violation" moves downstream to affect the completion condition at the last event.

FIGURE 7

Visual display of $L_3 = 10$:

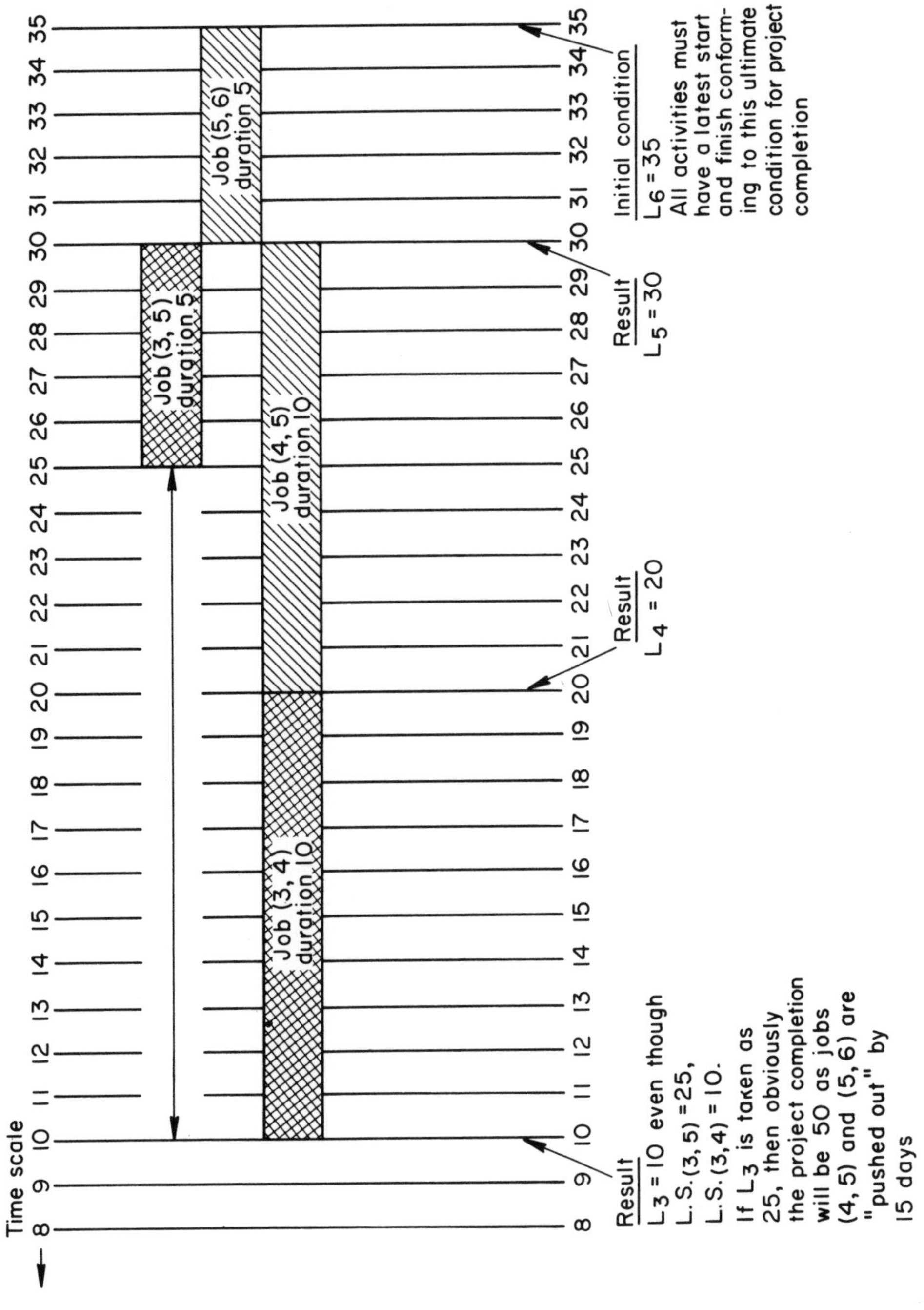

Time scale

8 9 10 11 12 13 14 15 16 17 18 19 20 21 22 23 24 25 26 27 28 29 30 31 32 33 34 35

Job (3, 4) duration 10

Job (3, 5) duration 5

Job (4, 5) duration 10

Job (5, 6) duration 5

Result
$L_3 = 10$ even though
L.S. (3, 5) = 25,
L.S. (3, 4) = 10.

If L_3 is taken as 25, then obviously the project completion will be 50 as jobs (4, 5) and (5, 6) are "pushed out" by 15 days

Result
$L_4 = 20$

Result
$L_5 = 30$

Initial condition
$L_6 = 35$
All activities must have a latest start and finish conforming to this ultimate condition for project completion

87

This leads to the rule:

$$L_{\text{current} \atop \text{event}} = \text{smallest of} \left\{ \begin{array}{l} \text{latest start times of} \\ \text{all jobs moving out of} \\ \text{the current event} \end{array} \right\}$$

Using the rule—

$$L_3 = \text{smaller of} \left\{ \begin{array}{l} \text{L.S.}_{(3,4)} = L_4 - D_{(3,4)} \\ \text{L.S.}_{(3,5)} = L_5 - D_{(3,5)} \end{array} \right\}$$

$$\begin{array}{l} = \text{smaller of} \left\{ \begin{array}{l} 20 - 10 = 10 \\ 30 - 5 = 25 \end{array} \right\} \\ = 10 \end{array}$$

Similarly, at event 2—

$$L_2 = \text{smallest of} \left\{ \begin{array}{l} \text{latest start of} \\ \text{all jobs out of} \\ \text{event 2} \end{array} \right\}$$

$$\begin{array}{l} = \text{smaller of} \left\{ \begin{array}{l} \text{L.S.}_{(2,3)} = L_3 - D_{(2,3)} = 10 - 5 = 5 \\ \text{L.S.}_{(2,4)} = L_4 - D_{(2,4)} = 20 - 5 = 15 \end{array} \right\} \\ = 5 \end{array}$$

These findings are shown in Figure 8.

FIGURE 8

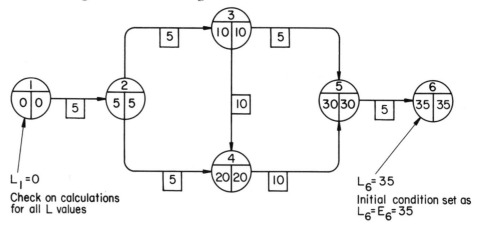

$L_1 = 0$

Check on calculations
for all L values

$L_6 = 35$

Initial condition set as
$L_6 = E_6 = 35$

Now (see Figure 8), at event 1 $L_1 = 0$, as is apparent by the rule—

$$\begin{array}{l} L_1 = [\text{smallest of L.S.}_{(1,2)}] \\ = L_2 - D_{(1,2)} \\ = 5 - 5 \\ = 0 \end{array}$$

This formula serves as a check on our arithmetic procedure in moving backward from the last event. Actually, it should be no surprise that the latest start of at least one job out of the first event is zero, since this fact was automatically imposed when the value of L for the last event was set.

A study of the results of the calculation for L will reveal the following:

1. At every event, the value of L gives the latest completion of activities that flow into (or precede) the event.

2. At every event, the value of L equals the latest starting time for at least one activity proceeding out of the event, *but not necessarily for all activities.* For instance, consider the result at event 3 in Figure 8 where $L_3 = 10$, but $L.S._{(3,5)} = 25$. It is unwise to look at the value of L at any particular event and use this value as the latest start for activities out of the event if there is more than one activity. The only sure way to find the latest start for jobs out of an event is to proceed to the end of each activity, take the value of L at that event, and subtract the duration.

This procedure is clearer if it is understood that every activity begins at one event and ends at another. We may refer to these as a "start event" and a "finish event." Then $L_{\text{start event}} = L.S._{\text{current activity}}$ for at least one activity, but not for all. This relationship can safely be used if only *one* activity proceeds from an event. Otherwise, it is better to use the relation—

$$L.S._{\substack{\text{current}\\\text{activity}}} = L_{\substack{\text{finish}\\\text{event}}} - D_{\substack{\text{current}\\\text{activity}}}$$

This is illustrated in Figure 9, which stems from Figure 8.

FIGURE 9

Activity	Duration	L starting event	L finish event = Latest finish	L.S. = L finish event – Duration	Remarks
1, 2	5	0	5	0	One job out of event 1; $L.S._{(1,2)} = L_1$
2, 3	5	5	10	5	Two jobs out of event 2; $L.S._{(2,3)} = L_2$ $L.S._{(2,4)} \neq L_2$
2, 4	5	5	20	15	
3, 4	10	10	20	10	Two jobs out of event 3 $L.S._{(3,4)} = L_3$ $L.S._{(3,5)} \neq L_3$
3, 5	5	10	30	25	
4, 5	10	20	30	20	One job out of event 4; $L.S._{(4,5)} = L_4$
5, 6	5	30	35	30	One job out of event 5; $L.S._{(5,6)} = L_5$

The outline should clarify the distinction between the values of L at the start and finish events and the latest start of an activity.

**Practical
Procedure**

Just as in the case of the earliest activity start, the rules for determining the latest finish time have been developed to provide a full knowledge of the meaning of the quantity. In real life the relations are not written down. The procedure is straightforward—what is usually done is to find the latest start for each job and mark it lightly on the diagram close to the appropriate event. Then, as we move backward by reverse sequence of event numbers, the smallest value at the event is written in as the value of L. This is illustrated in Figures 10 to 14.

FIGURE 10

Procedure at event 6:

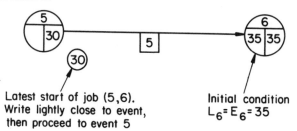

Latest start of job (5,6). Write lightly close to event, then proceed to event 5

Initial condition $L_6 = E_6 = 35$

FIGURE 11

Procedure at event 5:

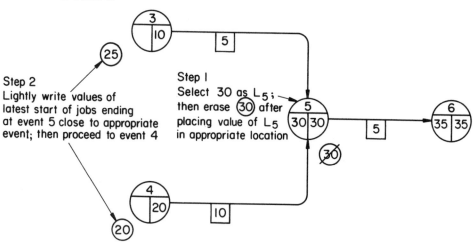

Step 2
Lightly write values of latest start of jobs ending at event 5 close to appropriate event; then proceed to event 4

Step 1
Select 30 as L_5; then erase ③⓪ after placing value of L_5 in appropriate location

FIGURE 12

Procedure at event 4:

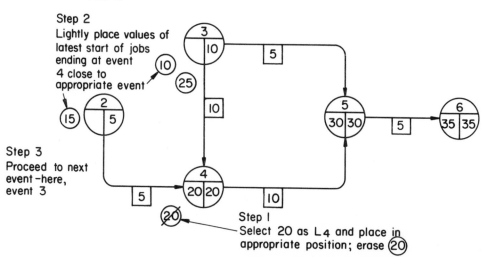

Step 2
Lightly place values of latest start of jobs ending at event 4 close to appropriate event

Step 3
Proceed to next event –here, event 3

Step 1
Select 20 as L_4 and place in appropriate position; erase ②⓪

90

FIGURE 13

Procedure at event 3:

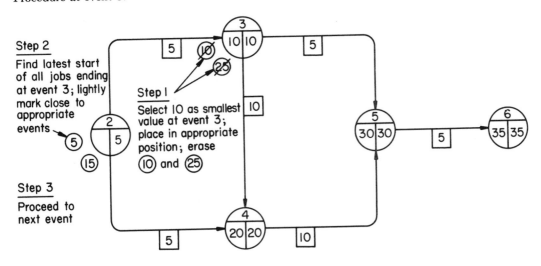

Step 2

Find latest start of all jobs ending at event 3; lightly mark close to appropriate events

Step 1

Select 10 as smallest value at event 3; place in appropriate position; erase 10 and 25

Step 3

Proceed to next event

FIGURE 14

Procedure at events 2 and 1:

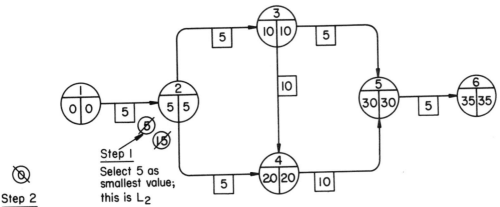

Step 1

Select 5 as smallest value; this is L_2

Step 2

Find latest start for job (1,2). Since this starts at the first event (last in backward direction), select value of $L_1 = 0$

The procedure for finding the latest activity start may be summarized as follows:

Summary of Rules

1. Latest start of an activity equals latest finish minus duration.

2. The latest finish of all jobs ending at the same event is represented by the symbol L.

3. The procedure starts by setting—

$$L_{\substack{\text{last} \\ \text{event}}} = E_{\substack{\text{last} \\ \text{event}}}$$

4. Values of L are found at each event by going backward in sequence from the last event to the first.

5. At each event—

$$L_{\substack{\text{current} \\ \text{event}}} = \text{smallest of} \begin{Bmatrix} \text{latest start} \\ \text{out of the} \\ \text{event} \end{Bmatrix}$$

This means that at any event the latest finish time of ending jobs will affect the start of all activities *out* of the event; thus the latest finish time of ending activities necessarily is numerically equal to the smallest value of the latest start for starting activities at that event. The procedure is as follows: At each event, starting at the last, find the latest start of all jobs ending at the event, marking these values *lightly* close to the label for the beginning event of each of these jobs. Then go on to the next event (in reverse sequence), select the smallest value of the latest start (take the smallest number), enter it in the proper location in the event label, erase the working numbers, find the latest start for all the jobs ending at the event, and so on.

6. $L_{\substack{\text{first} \\ \text{event}}} = E_{\substack{\text{first} \\ \text{event}}} = 0$

7. *L.S.* values can be picked off the diagram, or from a table of activities. It is always best to use the relation—

$$L.S. = L.F. - \text{duration}$$

Exercises

Find the values of L at each event in the six projects for which values of E were calculated in the exercises at the end of the previous chapter.

Solutions

1. Project 502:

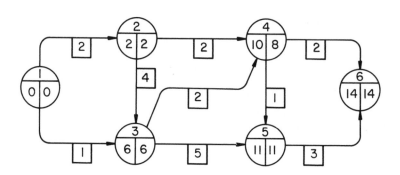

2. Project 503:

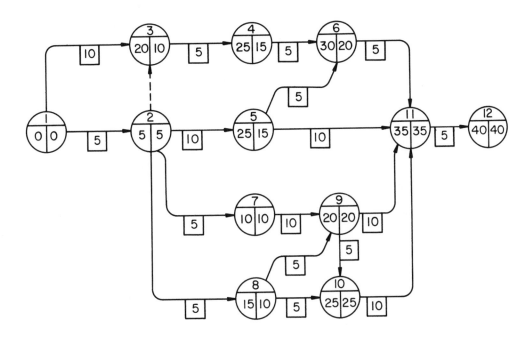

3. Project 504:

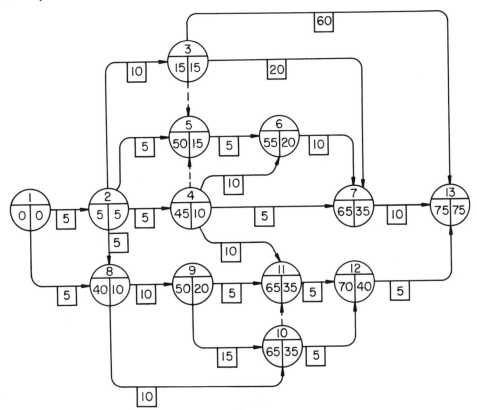

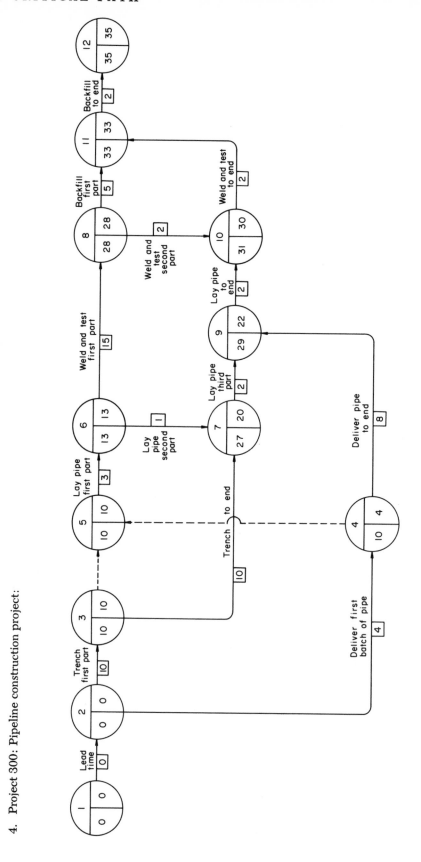

4. Project 300: Pipeline construction project:

5. Project 312: Arrow diagram for changing a flat tire:

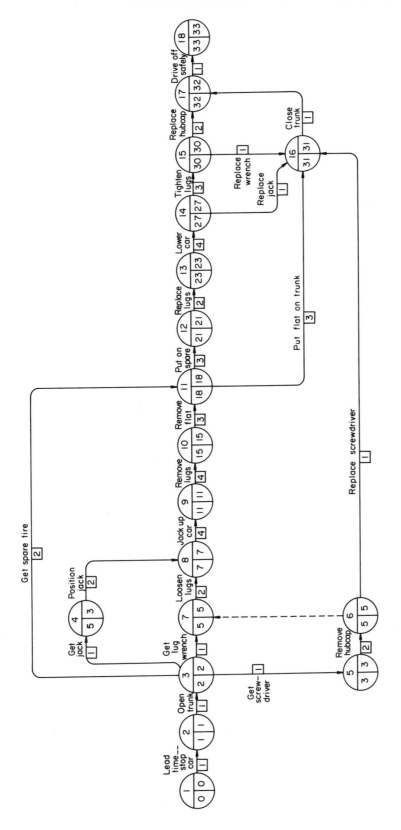

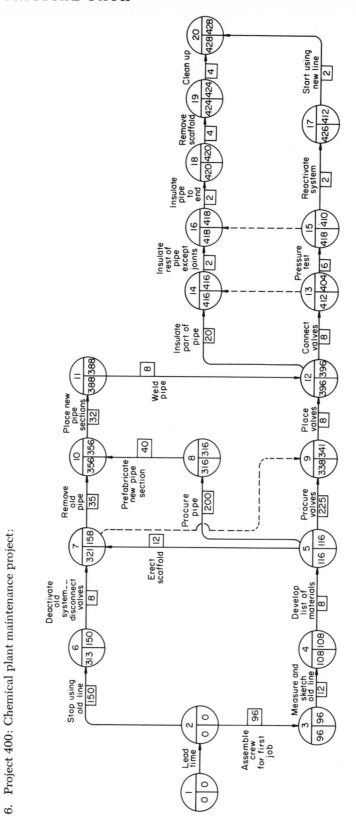

6. Project 400: Chemical plant maintenance project:

CHAPTER SIX

The Critical Path and Job Boundaries

WITH A KNOWLEDGE OF the earliest and latest starting times for each activity, it is possible to establish:

1. Whether or not a job is critical, and what is the critical path.
2. The actual variation of job starting time, or the job boundaries, for use in leveling resource allocation in scheduling.

In this chapter we shall be concerned with the concepts underlying the real meaning of the critical path as it applies to completing the project. Therefore, we shall emphasize analyzing the float, if any, of a job in relation to all other jobs in the project.

It will be recalled that the variation in starting times for a job is called "total float." From the calculation procedure detailed in the preceding chapter we have found that for any job—

Earliest start $= E_{\text{starting event}}$

and—

Latest start $= (L_{\text{ending event}}) - (\text{duration})$

Hence—

Total float $= (\text{latest start})$ less (earliest start)
$= (L_{\text{ending event}}) - (\text{duration}) - (E_{\text{starting event}})$

Consider Figure 1, which illustrates the situation at some general event. In order to simplify the terminology, rather than "starting event," the subscript T (tail of arrow) could be used. Similarly, instead of "ending event," the subscript H (head of arrow) could be used. We can then deal with the general activity represented by the notation (T, H), wherein the symbol T stands for the beginning event (or tail) of every activity and H for the ending event (or head). Now, the rule for numbering events is such that the event number at the tail of the arrow is always less than the number at the head. Hence, numerically, the value of T will always be less than the value of H. But T stands further along in the alphabet than H and might seem to imply that the numerical value of T is larger than the numerical value for H. This problem would not be present if T stood closer to A in the alphabet than H. A better way to select the general notation, therefore, is to select two letters of the alphabet other than T and H. For instance, if i and j are selected to represent, respectively, the tail and the head of the arrow, then, whenever the designation (i, j) is seen, it can be immediately understood as the equivalent of (tail, head), since i is of lower value (closer to A) than j, and since the number of the event at the tail is always less than the number at the head. The notation (i, j) will in fact be adopted for representation of the "general" activity and will be used henceforth, as it is in Figure 1.

FIGURE 1

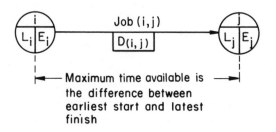

Maximum time available is the difference between earliest start and latest finish

Total Float

In terms of the (i, j) notation—

$$\text{Total float}_{(i,j)} = L_j - E_i - D_{(i,j)}$$

As shown in Figure 1, the maximum time available to perform any job is equal to the difference between the latest finish (L_j) and the earliest start (E_i). This is rather obvious, for if the required time, or job duration, is subtracted from the maximum time available, the result is the excess of the available over the required time. This is also equal to the total float. For any activity, then, the total float is defined as the excess of the available time over the required time of performance. The result of this excess time shows up in a possible variation of starting time. While it can be, and has been, shown that these statements are algebraically equivalent, it should really come as no surprise. Quite obviously, if there is any excess in available time to do the job, then there will be a variation in starting time, since we can delay the start of the job to the full extent of the excess available time. Just as obviously, the total float, or excess time, will show up as the difference of possible ending times. Consider what happens if we start a job at its earliest possible starting time and start succeeding jobs at their latest possible starts. The waiting time between the start of succeeding jobs and the end of the current job will be numerically equal to the difference between the earliest and latest finish for that job, and it will also be the possible excess time for that job; otherwise there would be no difference. The algebraic equivalence of these statements is shown below:

$$
\begin{aligned}
\text{Total float} &= \text{maximum available time} - (\text{duration}) \\
&= (\text{latest finish}) - (\text{earliest start}) - (\text{duration}) \\
&= (L_j - E_i) - \text{duration} \\
&= L_j - E_i - D_{(i,j)} \\
&= L_j - [E_i + D_{(i,j)}] = \text{latest finish} - \text{earliest finish} \\
&= [L_j - D_{(i,j)}] - E_i = \text{latest start} - \text{earliest start}
\end{aligned}
$$

Each of these relations is useful for specific purposes. The relation or definition of total float as the excess of available over required time is useful for understanding the true nature of total float. The relation in terms of difference in starting time is of importance in showing the use of float in scheduling. Total float as the difference of finish times, however, is the definition used for determining it and the critical path from the diagram.

The Critical Path

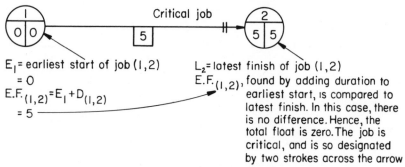

E_1 = earliest start of job (1,2)
    = 0
E.F.$_{(1,2)}$ = $E_1 + D_{(1,2)}$
    = 5

L_2 = latest finish of job (1,2)
E.F.$_{(1,2)}$, found by adding duration to earliest start, is compared to latest finish. In this case, there is no difference. Hence, the total float is zero. The job is critical, and is so designated by two strokes across the arrow

FIGURE 2

Consider Figure 2, where the practical procedure for finding float and marking critical jobs is illustrated. The critical path for Project 501 can be determined as shown in Figure 3.

Project 501. Critical path:

FIGURE 3

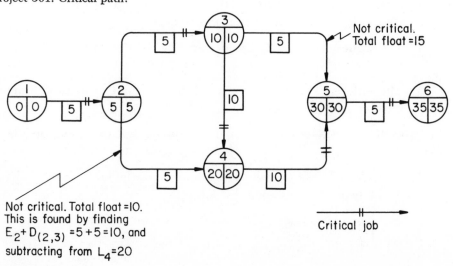

Not critical. Total float =15

Not critical. Total float =10. This is found by finding $E_2 + D_{(2,3)}$ = 5 + 5 = 10, and subtracting from L_4 = 20

Critical job

A study of Figure 3 suggests a rapid and practical way to find the critical path without finding the total float. Consider Figure 4, where the information for job (4,5) is displayed.

FIGURE 4

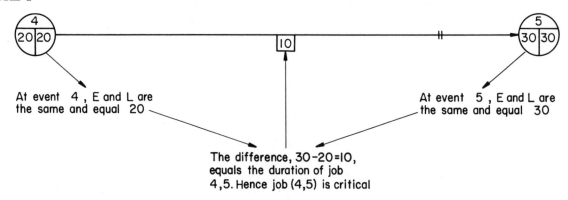

On the other hand, consider job (2,4) in Figure 5.

FIGURE 5

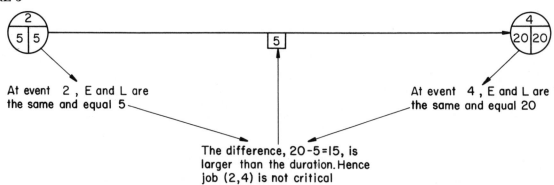

To illustrate the procedure further, take Project 700 as shown in Figure 6.

From a study of Projects 501 and 700 in Figures 3 and 6, it is evident that two conditions determine whether a job is critical:

1. The values of E and L are identical at the tail *and* at the head of that arrow.

2. The difference of the numbers at the tail and head of the arrow must equal the duration of the job.

The procedure for determining whether a job is critical, therefore, is as follows:

1. Consider jobs whose values of E and L are the same at the tail and at the head. For instance, for job (i,j)—
$$E_i = L_i$$
$$E_j = L_j$$
2. Find the difference.

100

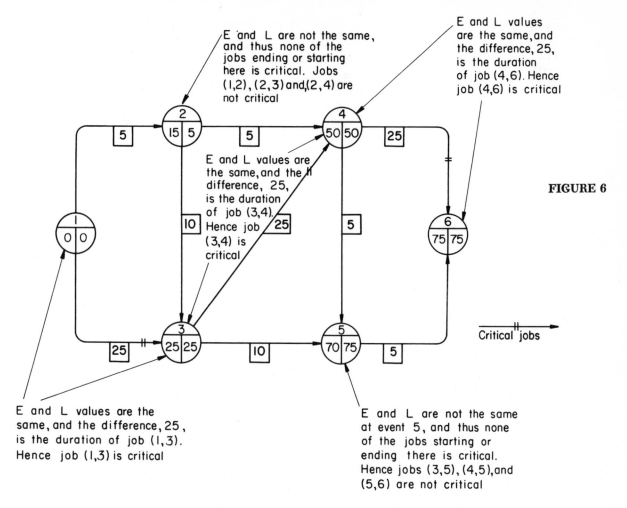

FIGURE 6

E and L are not the same, and thus none of the jobs ending or starting here is critical. Jobs (1,2), (2,3) and (2,4) are not critical

E and L values are the same, and the difference, 25, is the duration of job (4,6). Hence job (4,6) is critical

E and L values are the same, and the difference, 25, is the duration of job (3,4). Hence job (3,4) is critical

Critical jobs

E and L values are the same, and the difference, 25, is the duration of job (1,3). Hence job (1,3) is critical

E and L are not the same at event 5, and thus none of the jobs starting or ending there is critical. Hence jobs (3,5), (4,5), and (5,6) are not critical

3. If the difference equals the duration, the job is critical.* Otherwise, the job is not critical.

The validity of this approach can be seen from the following considerations:

1. For job (i,j), E_i is the earliest starting time, and its earliest finish is found by adding the duration. Thus—
   Earliest finish of job $(i,j) = E_i +$ duration

2. When a job is critical, it has no variation in starting time. For job (i,j) this means that—
   Earliest start = latest start, or
   E_i = $L_j -$ duration, or
   Duration = $L_j - E_i$

---

* This can be proved algebraically as follows: A job is critical if the total float is zero. Thus, for job (i,j)—

$$T.F._{(i,j)} = O = L_j - E_i - D_{(i,j)}$$

If $E_i = L_i$ and $E_j = L_j$, then

$$T.F._{(i,j)} = O = L_j - L_i - D_{(i,j)} = E_j - E_i - D_{(i,j)}$$
$$\text{or } L_j - L_i = D_{(i,j)}$$
$$\text{or } E_j - E_i = D_{(i,j)}$$

3. Now, at event j, if job (i,j) is critical, the latest finish of job (i,j) must equal the earliest start of all jobs immediately following— that is, starting at event j—otherwise float exists in job (i,j). That is to say, at event j—

$$L_j = E_j$$

4. As a result, for the case of job (i,j) being critical,

$$\text{Duration} = L_j - E_i = E_j - E_i$$

5. Similarly—

$$\text{Duration} = L_j - L_i$$

Total Float and the Critical Path

Total float is the excess of available time over required time, and it indicates by its very existence that there can be some latitude in scheduling the start of a non-critical job. The absence of float indicates that no leeway is possible in scheduling the start if the earliest project completion time is to be realized. If there is no float, the job is critical, and all of the critical jobs form the critical path. While there may be more than one critical path in a project, no job can be critical without lying on a critical path.

With this definition of critical jobs and critical path, certain things are immediately apparent.

1. The project duration equals the sum of the durations along one critical path from project start to project finish; that is, a critical path is the "longest chain" from beginning to end.

2. A delay in the start or finish of a critical job will delay the project completion by an equal amount.

3. If more resources are applied ("crashing") to reduce the project duration, then jobs must be selected from among those that are critical.

4. Priority of resource allocation must be given to critical jobs. If resources are unlimited, then the critical jobs are rigidly scheduled by their earliest possible start, and the non-critical jobs are scheduled to "level out" the resource levels.

The Meaning of Total Float

Take Project 700 (Figure 6) and the following values for three of the jobs in that project:

Job	Duration	Earliest		Latest		Total Float
		Start	Finish	Start	Finish	
(1,2)	5	0	5	10	15	10
(2,3)	10	5	15	15	25	10
(1,3)	25	0	25	0	25	0

These values have been used to prepare Figure 7.

Consider jobs (1,2) and (2,3) as a chain. Together they have a total duration of 15 time units (say, days), and the sum of their individual total
floats is 20. However, E_3, the earliest starting time of jobs (3,4) and (3,5),
is 25. Therefore, the time available to get jobs (1,2) and (2,3) done is
25 days. Their required time is 15 days, so the float is 10 days, but the
sum of the floats is 20 days!

There is no contradiction if we remember that the total float for each job
is a measure of its particular relationship to all other jobs in the project,
since the earliest activity start time ties in all preceding jobs and the latest
activity finish time ties in all succeeding jobs.

We should remember, in short, that the float in job (1,2) comes from its
relationship to other jobs, particularly to job (2,3). Consequently, if all
the float for job (1,2) is used, job (2,3) cannot start until its latest starting time, and it then has *no* total float. This situation is shown in Figure 7.

The total float of any specific activity has meaning only in relation to
other jobs in the project:

FIGURE 7

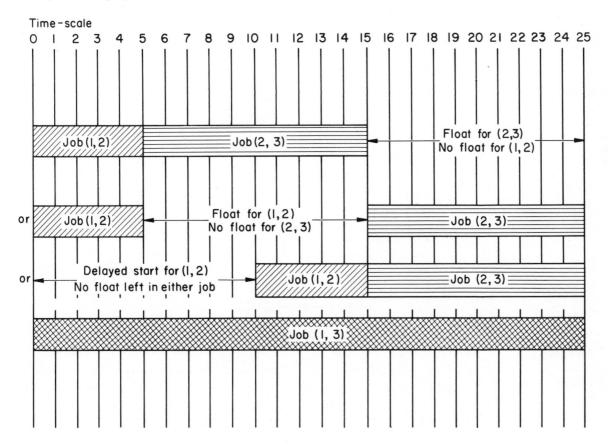

By the same token, if job (1,2) is started at its latest starting time (10),
once again job (2,3) cannot start until its latest starting time (15). In this
case, neither job has any total float after it is started. The situation may

be summarized by saying that a job with total float may interfere with the total float of succeeding jobs.

Consider next jobs (1,2) and (2,4) as a job chain. For these two jobs the following facts are pertinent: Let us assume that job (1,2) starts as late as possible, which is at time 10. Thus job (2,4) cannot start until time 15; and, with a duration of 5 and a latest finish of 50, it now has a total float of 30.

Job	Duration	Earliest		Latest		Total Float
		Start	Finish	Start	Finish	
(1,2)	5	0	5	10	15	10
(2,4)	5	5	10	45	50	40

Hence, delaying the start of job (1,2) until its latest starting time has given birth to a "downstream" interference factor in both jobs (2,3) and (2,4), and the amount of this interference is 10 units.

The situation concerning jobs (1,2), (2,3), and (2,4) of Project 700 is shown in Figure 8.

FIGURE 8   Project 700. Pertinent portion:

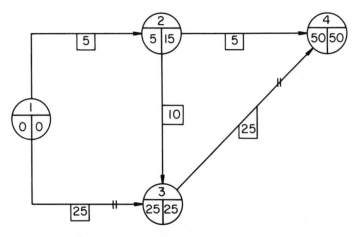

Interfering Float and Event Slack

At event 2, $E_2 = 5$ and $L_2 = 15$, meaning that jobs ending at 2 can end as late as time 15, but jobs starting there could start as early as time 5. There is an interference factor here of $L_2 - E_2 = 10$, which can be shifted "downstream." So, if job (1,2) ends at 15, the earliest *possible* start for (2,3) and (2,4) is 15, and not $E_2 = 5$.

The difference between the E and L values at any event is called "event slack." While it could be tabled as a function of the event, its true significance lies in the fact that it quantifies the potential downstream interference. As "interfering float," it is attached to each activity that ends at the event in question. We could say that event 2 has an event slack of 10, but it is more significant and meaningful to say that activity (1,2) has an interfering float of 10.

This apparent play on words may be clarified by reconsidering the reason for planning. We plan to determine resources and their order of commitment. We then schedule by allocating resources, according to the need shown in our plan, up to the limits available. The crux of the matter is quite simple: We are interested in an ultimate schedule that shows the proper allocation of resources. That means we will *schedule jobs—not events!* While event slack, as such, is interesting, it is not really useful in scheduling. However, if we select a starting time for some job which is later than its earliest possible start, then we are certainly interested in the possible downstream interference of our decision. Hence, even if we call it *event slack*, let us be certain to recognize that its real worth lies in its measure of interference.

Activity Orientation

There are some exponents of PERT who claim that event slack is, of itself, important in expediting to meet an imposed completion time. But, as we shall see later, we can never expedite an event—we can only expedite an activity. And we can only expedite a project if we expedite what we have to do.

There is usually little, if any, value in finding the event slack for the sole purpose of calculating some value. True, using it as interfering float on all jobs ending at that event could be useful. Experience has shown, however, that the only really useful float is total float.

This discussion, it is hoped, will be of assistance in clarifying the true nature of total float and in clarifying some of the literature on the subject of event slack.

Free Float

Consider Figure 9, showing the data for jobs (1,2) and (2,3) of Project 700. Job (1,2) can start as early as time 0, and job (2,3) can start as early as time 5. If job (2,3) starts at 5, the float of job (1,2) is zero.

The value of float when all jobs start as *early* as possible is called "free float." For job (1,2), then, the free float is zero.

FIGURE 9

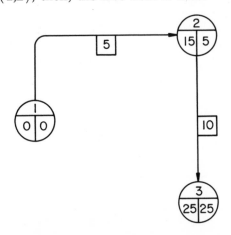

At event 3, succeeding jobs can start as early as time 25. Job (2,4) can start as early as time 5. The free float for job (2,4), then, is 20.

By definition, free float is the excess of available time over the required time (duration) *when all jobs start as early as possible*. By formula, then—

Free float for job (i,j) = $E_j - E_i -$ duration of job (i,j).

Consider job (1,2). It has a total float of 10 and a free float of 0. Furthermore, it has an interfering float of 10 (event slack of 10 at its ending event, No. 2). The value of the interfering float was found by determining that succeeding jobs could start at time 5 ($E_2 = 5$), while job (1,2) could end as late as time 15 ($L_2 = 15$). But the free float was found by ignoring the fact that job (1,2) could end at time 15 ($L_2 = 15$) and concentrating on the fact that job (1,2) could start at time 0 ($E_1 = 0$) and that job (2,4) could start at time 5 ($E_2 = 5$).

Hence, free float plus interfering float equals total float. Algebraically, we can express it as follows:

$$
\begin{aligned}
\text{Total float} &= L_j - E_i - \text{duration} \\
&= E_j - E_j + L_j - E_i - \text{duration} \\
&= (E_j - E_i - \text{duration}) + (L_j - E_j) \\
&= \text{free float} + \text{interfering float}
\end{aligned}
$$

and illustrate this formula in Figures 10(a), 10(b), and 11.

FIGURE 10(a)

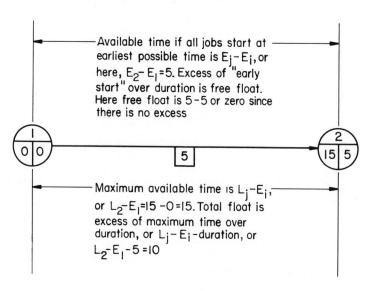

Available time if all jobs start at earliest possible time is $E_j - E_i$, or here, $E_2 - E_1 = 5$. Excess of "early start" over duration is free float. Here free float is 5−5 or zero since there is no excess

Maximum available time is $L_j - E_i$, or $L_2 - E_1 = 15 - 0 = 15$. Total float is excess of maximum time over duration, or $L_j - E_i -$ duration, or $L_2 - E_1 - 5 = 10$

FIGURE 10(b)

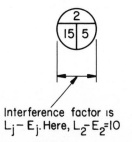

Interference factor is $L_j - E_j$. Here, $L_2 - E_2 = 10$

Relationship of total float, free float, and interfering float:

FIGURE 11

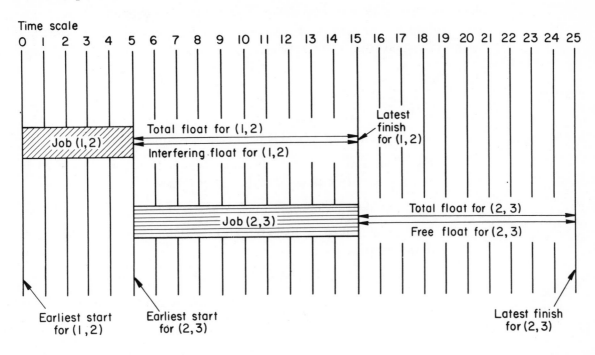

So far, for any job, we have considered:

Independent Float

1. Starting as early as possible or ending as late as possible to find total float.
2. Starting all jobs as early as possible to find free float.

Is there any advantage to finding out what excess exists if all the preceding jobs end as *late* as possible and all succeeding jobs start as *early* as possible?

Independent float:

FIGURE 12

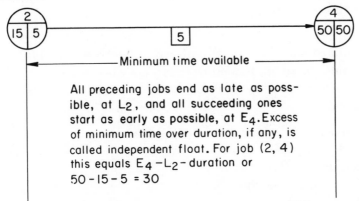

Consider job (2,4) of Project 700 in Figure 12. We define "independent float" as the excess of minimum available time over the required time (duration). Independent float is a useful quantity to evaluate since it provides a measure of variation in job-starting time without affecting any other job in the project. By this we mean that if an activity has independent float, its starting time can be delayed up to its limit without affecting any other job in the project. As we have seen before, however, this does not necessarily hold true for total float.

Summary of Floats

1. Total float is the excess of the *maximum available* time over duration; thus—

$$\text{Total float of job } (i,j) = L_j - E_i - \text{duration}$$

2. Free float is the excess of available time over required time when *all jobs start as early as possible;* thus—

$$\text{Free float of job } (i,j) = E_j - E_i - \text{duration}$$

3. Independent float is the excess of *minimum available* time over duration; thus—

$$\text{Independent float of job } (i,j) = E_j - L_i - \text{duration}$$

4. Interfering float is the potential downstream interference of any job; it is equal to the difference between total float and free float; thus—

$$
\begin{aligned}
\text{Interfering float for job } (i,j) \\
&= (\text{total float})_{(i,j)} - (\text{free float})_{(i,j)} \\
&= (L_j - E_i - \text{duration}) - (E_j - E_i - \text{duration}) \\
&= L_j - E_j \\
&= \text{event slack at event } j.
\end{aligned}
$$

5. Event slack at any event is the difference between the E and L values at that event. The symbol S is used to represent event slack. Hence—

$$S_j = L_j - E_j$$

is the slack at event j.

Job Boundaries

While total float and the critical path can be determined entirely from an arrow diagram, there are numerous occasions when a tabular listing of job boundaries would be quite useful. The items of interest constituting any job's boundaries are:

1. Sequence code: activity designation in terms of the event numbers at the tail and head of each arrow; that is, the i and j designation of each job *(i,j)*.
2. A description of the job.
3. The duration.
4. The earliest start and finish.
5. The latest start and finish.
6. The float, if any.
7. The cost.

8. The resource requirements.
9. The scheduled start and finish.

Up to this point in our text we have learned how to handle all of these boundaries except cost, resource requirements, and scheduled start and finish. We can thus create, for any project, a tabular listing with the headings:

1. Job sequence, (i,j).
2. Description.
3. Duration, $D_{(i,j)}$.
4. Earliest start, E_i.
5. Earliest finish, $E_i + D_{(i,j)}$.
6. Latest start, $L_j - D_{(i,j)}$.
7. Latest finish, L_j.
8. Total float.
9. Other floats.

Event Tables

Since so many of the values required for a job boundary listing are concerned with the values of E and L, a listing of these values, and of the event slack, will be helpful. They are shown in Table 1 for Project 501 (Figure 3).

Project 501. Event table:

TABLE 1

Event Number	E	L	Event* Slack S = L - E
1	0	0	0
2	5	5	0
3	10	10	0
4	20	20	0
5	30	30	0
6	35	35	0

*NOTE: Event slack is also interfering float for all jobs ending at the event in question; that is, at event j, the event slack equals interfering float of job (i,j).

From the information contained in Figure 3 and in Table 1, the job boundaries of Project 501 can be derived; they are listed in Table 2. Note that descriptions have been omitted for the sake of simplicity.

Job Boundary Tables

TABLE 2

Col. 1 Job Sequence (i, j)	Col. 2 Duration $D_{(i, j)}$	Col. 3 Earliest Start	Col. 4 Earliest Finish	Col. 5 Latest Start	Col. 6 Latest Finish	Col. 7 Total Float	Col. 8 Free Float	Col. 9 Independent Float
1,2	5	0	5	0	5	0	0	0
2,3	5	5	10	5	10	0	0	0
2,4	5	5	10	15	20	10	10	10
3,4	10	10	20	10	20	0	0	0
3,5	5	10	15	25	30	15	15	15
4,5	10	20	30	20	30	0	0	0
5,6	5	30	35	30	35	0	0	0

The values in Table 2 were found by the following procedure.

Step 1. Column 1, the sequence code, is completed first by listing all jobs in ascending order of the start event and, within each value of the start event, by ascending value of the ending event. That is, all jobs are sorted by ascending values of i and, within each value of i, by ascending values of j. This is called a "sorted sequence" in ascending order on i major, j minor.

For Project 501 jobs are sorted on 1, 2, 3, 4, and 5 as values of i. At event 2 two jobs start—(2,3) and (2,4). In this case the possible j values are 3 and 4. Hence, the sorting puts job (2,3) before job (2,4). The same is true at event 3, with the result that job (3,4) is listed before job (3,5).

Step 2. Column 2, duration, is completed next by listing values of the duration of each job opposite the appropriate job sequence code. Values of duration are placed directly in Column 2 from a specially prepared list or read from the arrow diagram.

Step 3. Column 3, earliest start, is completed by reading values of E from the diagram or from the event table. We can do this rapidly since the same numeric value applies as the starting time for all jobs with the same i; that is, E_i is the earliest start for all jobs out of event i. For example, since in Figure 3 $E_2 = 5$, then 5 is placed as the earliest start for both jobs (2,3) and (2,4). This is at once visually evident because all jobs are sorted in i sequence.

Step 4. Column 4, earliest finish, is found directly by adding together the entries in Columns 2 and 3, duration and earliest start.

Step 5. Column 6, latest finish, is completed by reading the value of L off the diagram or from the event table and placing it in all rows with the j value of the activity identical to the event number at which the value of L is selected. For instance, in Figure 3, reading $L_4 = 20$, we place the latest finish value of 20 in Column 6, opposite jobs (2,4) and (3,4).

In this case, the visual scanning is more difficult, since we are searching the table on *j*. However, omissions are easily evident and can be readily corrected by finding the appropriate value of *L* from the diagram.

Step 6. Column 5, latest start, is completed by subtracting the entries in Column 2 from those in Column 6; that is, subtracting duration from latest finish.

Step 7. Next is Column 7, total float. There are four ways of finding total float. All are equivalent, and all lead to the same answer. The first two are the best.

- **Method 1:** Total float is the difference in starting times, which means that total float is the latest start minus the earliest start, or Column 5 minus Column 3.

- **Method 2:** Total float is the difference in finish times; in other words, total float is the latest finish minus the earliest finish, or Column 6 minus Column 4.

- **Method 3:** By definition, total float is the excess of available time over the required time, which is the latest finish less the earliest start less the duration—or Column 6 minus Column 3 minus Column 2.

- **Method 4:** Total float for each job may be read directly from the diagram. This is virtually equivalent to Method 3.

Step 8. Free float is completed by subtracting the interfering float. Thus, for job *(i,j)*—

$$\text{Free float of job } (i,j) = [\text{total float of job } (i,j)] \text{ less } \begin{Bmatrix} \text{event slack} \\ \text{at event } j \end{Bmatrix}$$
$$= (\text{total float})_{(i,j)} - S_j$$

Step 9. Independent float is completed by reference to the diagram and the formula:

$$\text{Independent float of job } (i,j) = E_j - L_i - \text{duration}$$

Alternatively—

$$\text{Independent float of job } (i,j) = [\text{free float of job } (i,j)]$$
$$\text{less } \begin{Bmatrix} \text{event slack} \\ \text{at event } i \end{Bmatrix} = (\text{free float})_{(i,j)} - S_i$$

This latter relation may be proved algebraically as follows:

$$\begin{aligned} \text{Independent float of job } (i,j) &= E_j - L_i - \text{duration} \\ &= E_j - E_i - \text{duration} + E_i - L_i \\ &= (\text{free float})_{(i,j)} - (L_i - E_i) \\ &= (\text{free float})_{(i,j)} - (\text{event slack})_i \end{aligned}$$

Note that if a negative value is produced, then the independent float is defined as zero.

To further illustrate the tabular listing procedures, the event tables and job boundaries for Project 700 (see Figure 6) have been completed and are displayed in Tables 3 and 4 below.

TABLE 3 Project 700. Event table:

Event Number	E	L	Event Slack S=L-E
1	0	0	0
2	5	15	10
3	25	25	0
4	50	50	0
5	55	70	15
6	75	75	0

TABLE 4 Project 700. Job boundaries:

Sequence Code (i,j)	Duration D(i,j)	Earliest Start	Earliest Finish	Latest Start	Latest Finish	Float Total	Float Free	Float Independent
1 , 2	5	0	5	10	15	10	0	0
1 , 3	25	0	25	0	25	0	0	0
2 , 3	10	5	15	15	25	10	10	0
2 , 4	5	5	10	45	50	40	40	30
3 , 4	25	25	50	25	50	0	0	0
3 , 5	10	25	35	60	70	35	20	20
4 , 5	5	50	55	65	70	15	0	0
4 , 6	25	50	75	50	75	0	0	0
5 , 6	5	55	60	70	75	15	15	0

Quite obviously—

1. Independent float is always equal to or less than free float.

2. Free float is always equal to or less than total float.

Summary

1. The "general" activity is represented as job (i,j).

2. At event i, earliest start of all succeeding jobs is E_i, where—

$$E_{\text{first event}} = 0$$

$$E_i = \text{largest} \left\{ \begin{array}{l} \text{earliest finish of} \\ \text{all jobs starting at } i \end{array} \right\}$$

$$E_{\text{last event}} = \text{project duration}$$

3. At event j, latest finish of all preceding jobs is L_j, where—

$$L_{\text{last event}} = E_{\text{last event}}$$

$$L_j = \text{smallest} \left\{ \begin{array}{l} \text{latest finish of} \\ \text{all jobs ending at } j \end{array} \right\}$$

$$L_{\text{first event}} = 0$$

4. Total float is the excess of available over required time and shows up as a range of starting times and (equally) a range of finish times. Where the float is zero, the job is critical and can be so marked on the diagram.

5. Job boundary tables can be completed by reading values of duration, E, and L from the diagram, or from an event listing, and then completing the other columns.

6. Event slack is represented by the symbol S, and $S = L - E$ at each event.

7. Free float for any job (i,j) is found by subtracting S_j from the total float.

8. Independent float for any job (i,j) is found by subtracting S_i from the free float.

For each of the six problem projects, Nos. 502, 503, 504, 300 (pipeline), 312 (flat tire), and 400 (plant maintenance), find—

Exercises

1. The critical path.

2. The event table. For each event, tabulate—

   The event number.
   E at that event.
   L at that event.
   Event slack, $S(L - E)$.

3. The job boundaries; for each activity, tabulate—

   Sequence code (i,j).
   Description (for Projects 300, 312, and 400 only).
   Duration.
   Earliest start.
   Earliest finish.
   Latest start.
   Latest finish.
   Total float.
   Free float (optional).
   Independent float (optional).

FINDING THE CRITICAL PATH

Solutions   1. Project 502:

(a) Critical path:

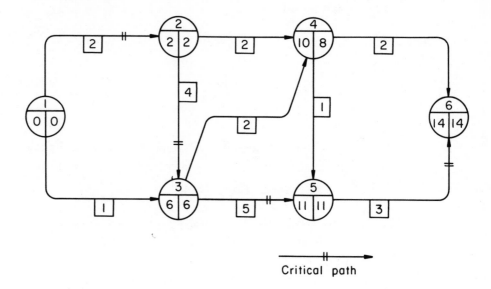

Critical   path

(b) Event table:

No.	E	L	S
1	0	0	0
2	2	2	0
3	6	6	0
4	8	10	2
5	11	11	0
6	14	14	0

(c) Job boundaries:

	Sequence		Duration	Earliest		Latest		Float		
	i	j		Start	Finish	Start	Finish	Total	Free	Inde-pendent
1	1	2	2	0	2	0	2	0	0	0
2	1	3	1	0	1	5	6	5	5	5
3	2	3	4	2	6	2	6	0	0	0
4	2	4	2	2	4	8	10	6	4	4
5	3	4	2	6	8	8	10	2	0	0
6	3	5	5	6	11	6	11	0	0	0
7	4	5	1	8	9	10	11	2	2	0
8	4	6	2	8	10	12	14	4	4	2
9	5	6	3	11	14	11	14	0	0	0

2. Project 503:

(a) Critical path:

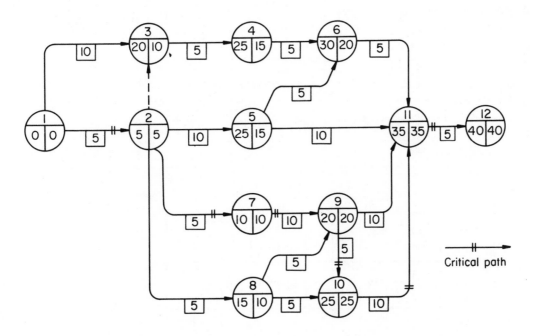

115

(c) Job boundaries:

Sequence i	j	Duration	Earliest Start	Earliest Finish	Latest Start	Latest Finish	Total	Free	Independent
1	2	5	0	5	0	5	0	0	0
1	3	10	0	10	10	20	10	0	0
2	3	0	5	5	20	20	15	5	5
2	5	10	5	15	15	25	10	0	0
2	7	5	5	10	5	10	0	0	0
2	8	5	5	10	10	15	5	0	0
3	4	5	10	15	20	25	10	0	0
4	6	5	15	20	25	30	10	0	0
5	6	5	15	20	25	30	10	0	0
5	11	10	15	25	25	35	10	10	0
6	11	5	20	25	30	35	10	10	0
7	9	10	10	20	10	20	0	0	0
8	9	5	10	15	15	20	5	5	5
8	10	5	10	15	20	25	10	10	0
9	10	5	20	25	20	25	0	0	0
9	11	10	20	30	25	35	5	5	5
10	11	10	25	35	25	35	0	0	0
11	12	5	35	40	35	40	0	0	0

(b) Event table:

No.	E	L	S
1	0	0	0
2	5	5	0
3	10	20	10
4	15	25	10
5	15	25	10
6	20	30	10
7	10	10	0
8	10	15	5
9	20	20	0
10	25	25	0
11	35	35	0
12	40	40	0

116

3. Project 504:

(a) Critical path:

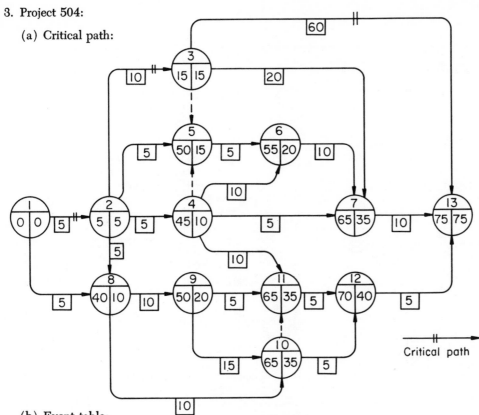

(b) Event table:

No.	E	L	S
1	0	0	0
2	5	5	0
3	15	15	0
4	10	45	35
5	15	50	35
6	20	55	35
7	35	65	30
8	10	40	30
9	20	50	30
10	35	65	30
11	35	65	30
12	40	70	30
13	75	75	0

FINDING THE CRITICAL PATH

(c) Job boundaries:

	Sequence		Duration	Earliest		Latest		Float		
	i	j		Start	Finish	Start	Finish	Total	Free	Inde-pendent
1	1	2	5	0	5	0	5	0	0	0
2	1	8	5	0	5	35	40	35	5	5
3	2	3	10	5	15	5	15	0	0	0
4	2	4	5	5	10	40	45	35	0	0
5	2	5	5	5	10	45	50	40	5	5
6	2	8	5	5	10	35	40	30	0	0
7	3	5	0	15	15	50	50	35	0	0
8	3	7	20	15	35	45	65	30	0	0
9	3	13	60	15	75	15	75	0	0	0
10	4	5	0	10	10	50	50	40	5	0
11	4	6	10	10	20	45	55	35	0	0
12	4	7	5	10	15	60	65	50	20	0
13	4	11	10	10	20	55	65	45	15	0
14	5	6	5	15	20	50	55	35	0	0
15	6	7	10	20	30	55	65	35	5	0
16	7	13	10	35	45	65	75	30	30	0
17	8	9	10	10	20	40	50	30	0	0
18	8	10	10	10	20	55	65	45	15	0
19	9	10	15	20	35	50	65	30	0	0
20	9	11	5	20	25	60	65	40	10	0
21	10	11	0	35	35	65	65	30	0	0
22	10	12	5	35	40	65	70	30	0	0
23	11	12	5	35	40	65	70	30	0	0
24	12	13	5	40	45	70	75	30	30	0

4. Project 300. Pipeline construction:

(a) Critical path:

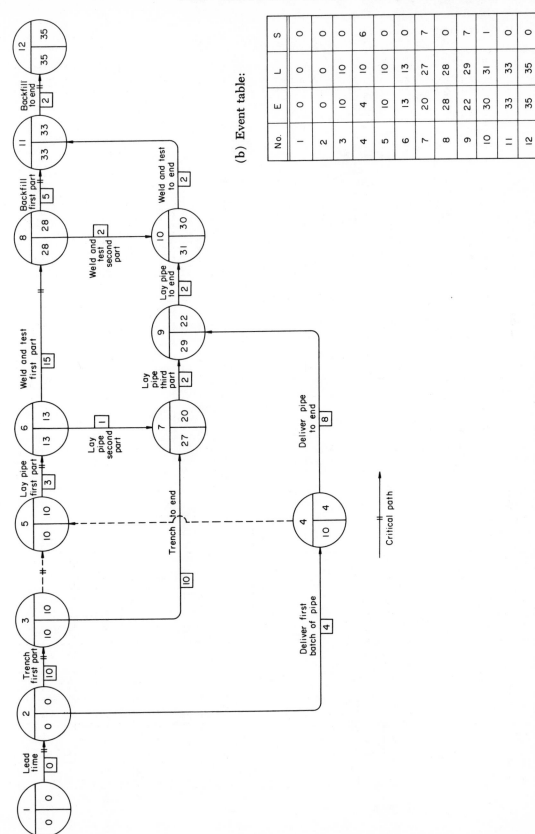

(b) Event table:

No.	E	L	S
1	0	0	0
2	0	0	0
3	10	10	0
4	4	10	6
5	10	10	0
6	13	13	0
7	20	27	7
8	28	28	0
9	22	29	7
10	30	31	1
11	33	33	0
12	35	35	0

(c) Job boundaries:

	Sequence		Description	Duration	Earliest		Latest		Float		
	i	j			Start	Finish	Start	Finish	Total	Free	Inde-pendent
1	1	2	Lead time	0	0	0	0	0	0	0	0
2	2	3	Trench first part	10	0	10	0	10	0	0	0
3	2	4	Deliver first batch pipe	4	0	4	6	10	6	0	0
4	3	5	Dummy	0	10	10	10	10	0	0	0
5	3	7	Trench to end	10	10	20	17	27	7	0	0
6	4	5	Dummy	0	4	4	10	10	6	6	0
7	4	9	Deliver pipe to end	8	4	12	21	29	17	10	4
8	5	6	Lay pipe first part	3	10	13	10	13	0	0	0
9	6	7	Lay pipe second part	1	13	14	26	27	13	6	6
10	6	8	Weld and test first part	15	13	28	13	28	0	0	0
11	7	9	Lay pipe third part	2	20	22	27	29	7	0	0
12	8	10	Weld and test second part	2	28	30	29	31	1	0	0
13	8	11	Backfill first part	5	28	33	28	33	0	0	0
14	9	10	Lay pipe to end	2	22	24	29	31	7	6	0
15	10	11	Weld and test to end	2	30	32	31	33	1	1	0
16	11	12	Backfill to end	2	33	35	33	35	0	0	0

120

5. Project 312. Changing a flat tire:

(a) Critical path:

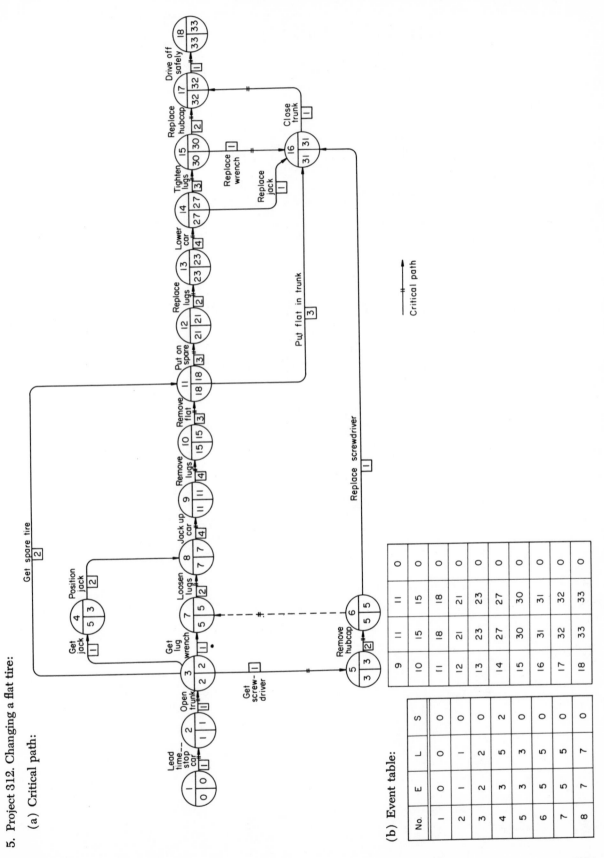

(b) Event table:

No.	E	L	S		No.	E	L	S
1	0	0	0		9	11	11	0
2	1	1	0		10	15	15	0
3	2	2	0		11	18	18	0
4	3	5	2		12	21	21	0
5	3	3	0		13	23	23	0
6	5	5	0		14	27	27	0
7	5	5	0		15	30	30	0
8	7	7	0		16	31	31	0
					17	32	32	0
					18	33	33	0

(c) Job boundaries:

#	Sequence i	Sequence j	Description	Duration	Earliest Start	Earliest Finish	Latest Start	Latest Finish	Float Total	Float Free	Float Independent
1	1	2	Lead time -- stop car	1	0	1	0	1	0	0	0
2	2	3	Open trunk	1	1	2	1	2	0	0	0
3	3	4	Get jack	1	2	3	4	5	2	0	0
4	3	5	Get screwdriver	1	2	3	2	3	0	0	0
5	3	7	Get lug wrench	1	2	3	4	5	2	2	2
6	3	11	Get spare tire	2	2	4	16	18	14	14	14
7	4	8	Position jack	2	3	5	5	7	2	2	0
8	5	6	Remove hubcap	2	3	5	3	5	0	0	0
9	6	7	Dummy	0	5	5	5	5	0	0	0
10	6	16	Replace screwdriver	1	5	6	30	31	25	25	25
11	7	8	Loosen lugs	2	5	7	5	7	0	0	0
12	8	9	Jack up car	4	7	11	7	11	0	0	0
13	9	10	Remove lugs	4	11	15	11	15	0	0	0
14	10	11	Remove flat	3	15	18	15	18	0	0	0
15	11	12	Put on spare	3	18	21	18	21	0	0	0
16	11	16	Put flat in trunk	3	18	21	28	31	10	10	10
17	12	13	Replace lugs	2	21	23	21	23	0	0	0
18	13	14	Lower car	4	23	27	23	27	0	0	0
19	14	15	Tighten lugs	3	27	30	27	30	0	0	0
20	14	16	Replace jack	1	27	28	30	31	3	3	3
21	15	16	Replace wrench	1	30	31	30	31	0	0	0
22	15	17	Replace hubcap	2	30	32	30	32	0	0	0
23	16	17	Close trunk	1	31	32	31	32	0	0	0
24	17	18	Drive off safely	1	32	33	32	33	0	0	0

6. Project 400. Chemical plant maintenance:

(a) Critical path:

(b) Event table:

No.	E	L	S
1	0	0	0
2	0	0	0
3	96	96	0
4	108	108	0
5	116	116	0
6	150	313	163
7	158	321	163
8	316	316	0
9	341	388	47
10	356	356	0
11	388	388	0
12	396	396	0
13	404	412	8
14	416	416	0
15	410	418	8
16	418	418	0
17	412	426	14
18	420	420	0
19	424	424	0
20	428	428	0

123

FINDING THE CRITICAL PATH

(c) Job boundaries:

	Sequence		Description	Duration	Earliest		Latest		Float		
	i	j			Start	Finish	Start	Finish	Total	Free	Inde-pendent
1	1	2	Lead time	0	0	0	0	0	0	0	0
2	2	3	Assemble crew	96	0	96	0	96	0	0	0
3	2	6	Stop using old line	150	0	150	163	313	163	0	0
4	3	4	Measure and sketch old line	12	96	108	96	108	0	0	0
5	4	5	Develop list materials	8	108	116	108	116	0	0	0
6	5	7	Erect scaffold	12	116	128	309	321	193	30	30
7	5	8	Procure pipe	200	116	316	116	316	0	0	0
8	5	9	Procure valves	225	116	341	163	388	47	0	0
9	6	7	Deactivate old line	8	150	158	313	321	163	0	0
10	7	9	Dummy	0	158	158	388	388	230	183	20
11	7	10	Remove old pipe	35	158	193	321	356	163	163	0
12	8	10	Prefabricate new pipe sections	40	316	356	316	356	0	0	0
13	9	12	Place valves	8	341	349	388	396	47	47	0
14	10	11	Place new pipe sections	32	356	388	356	388	0	0	0
15	11	12	Weld pipe	8	388	396	388	396	0	0	0
16	12	13	Insulate part of pipe	20	396	416	396	416	0	0	0
17	12	14	Connect valves	8	396	404	404	412	8	8	8
18	13	14	Dummy	0	404	404	416	416	12	12	4
19	13	15	Pressure test	6	404	410	412	418	8	0	0
20	14	16	Insulate, except joints	2	416	418	416	418	0	0	0
21	15	16	Dummy	0	410	410	418	418	0	0	0
22	15	17	Reactivate system	2	410	412	424	426	14	0	0
23	16	18	Insulate, pipe to end	2	418	420	418	420	0	0	0
24	17	20	Start using new line	2	412	414	426	428	14	14	0
25	18	19	Remove scaffold	4	420	424	420	424	0	0	0
26	19	20	Clean up	4	424	428	424	428	0	0	0

CHAPTER SEVEN

Milestone Networks

So FAR WE HAVE CONSIDERED only activity-oriented (arrow) diagrams; that is, those in which arrows representing activities are connected to form a diagram model of the project. Another way of modeling a project is to select its milestones, or key events, and link them together. In this case the arrows represent the expected duration between events, and the result is an event-oriented diagram.

The pipeline construction project, No. 300, will be used to illustrate how to create a milestone network. This particular project consists of digging a trench, placing pipe sections in the trench, welding and testing the weld of the sections, and then filling the trench. The project starts with trenching and ends when the backfilling is complete. The milestones of this project are:

The Pipeline Construction Project

- (Start project).
- (End trenching).
- (End laying pipe).
- (End weld and test).
- (End project).

These can be linked together with arrows to produce a network, as shown in Figure 1. The arrows represent elapsed time during which work of some kind is being done.

FIGURE 1   Milestones are connected to arrows representing elapsed time; the result is an event-oriented diagram:

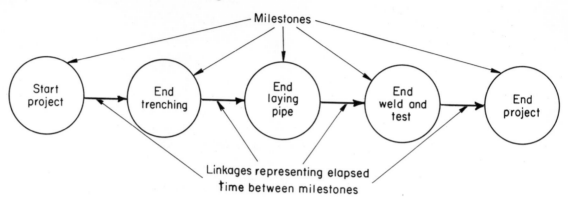

Let us now introduce the fact that pipe must be available for the pipelaying function. We are interested, then, in two further milestones: (pipe available) and (pipe delivery ends). We are assuming a continuous delivery of pipe to meet job requirements. Hence, the times of the first delivery and of the completion of all deliveries are pertinent. These milestones can be added to the network, as has been done in Figure 2.

The delivery of pipe *must* be connected to the overall pipelaying operation, and so we must include a further milestone in our network: (start laying pipe). Then, using a dummy (no elapsed time) arrow, we can show that having some pipe on hand is a prerequisite of starting to lay the pipe in the trench. Furthermore, the last delivery of pipe must be made at some time between the first pipe delivery and the completion of the pipelaying operation. This too is shown in Figure 2.

FIGURE 2   Pipe delivery milestones connected to work milestones where pipe is used:

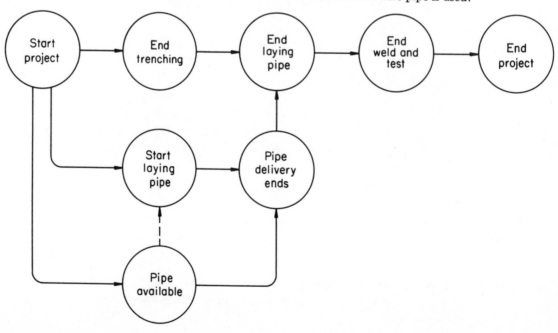

Further study of Figure 2 shows that there must be some elapsed time between the start of the project and the start of pipelaying, since, quite obviously, some trenching must be complete before the pipelaying can begin. This accounts for the arrow, representing elapsed time, between (start project), which is the start of trenching, and (start laying pipe).

This event-oriented diagram can now be numbered (see Figure 3). The numbering procedure is identical with that employed for activity-oriented arrow diagrams. In other words, it is good practice to number the events so that the event number at the tail of an arrow is less than the event number at its head. (For reasons that will become apparent later in this chapter, certain numbers have been omitted from the diagram.)

Milestone or event-oriented network with numbered events: **FIGURE 3**

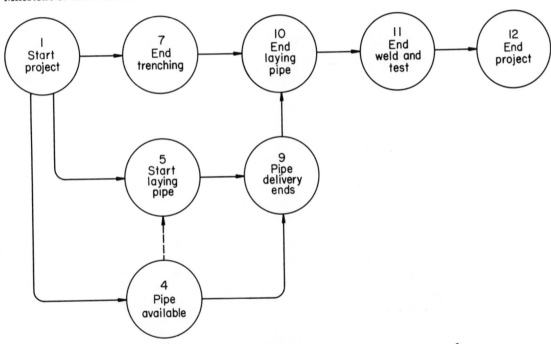

For an *observer* the network shown in Figure 3 appears to be quite adequate. By determining the expected completion of an event or its arrival at any particular milestone he can tell at a glance whether or not the project is "on time" or "late."

In order to use such a network gainfully, however, we must be sure that two conditions are met:

1. That the linkages are correct.
2. That the calculated values of expected event completions are correct.

Let us examine the validity of these assumptions. As a first step, we shall find the expected project duration and the critical path. To do this, durations are required.

The Critical Path

Let us assume that the durations shown in Table 1 apply to the pipeline construction project.

> ## Table 1
>
> 1. The entire trenching function takes 20 time units.
>
> 2. The entire pipelaying function takes 8 time units.
>
> 3. The entire weld and test function takes 19 time units.
>
> 4. The entire backfill function takes 7 time units.
>
> 5. The entire delivery function takes 12 time units.
>
> 6. The first delivery will take 4 time units.
>
> 7. Pipelaying starts 10 time units after trenching.
>
> 8. Weld and test starts 3 time units after pipelaying.
>
> 9. Backfilling starts 15 time units after weld and test.
>
> 10. Trenching ends 4 time units before pipelaying.
>
> 11. Pipelaying ends 2 time units before weld and test.
>
> 12. Weld and test ends 2 time units before backfill.
>
> 13. The last pipe delivery is made 2 time units before pipelaying ends.

FIGURE 4   Duration of pipelaying project is 28 time units:

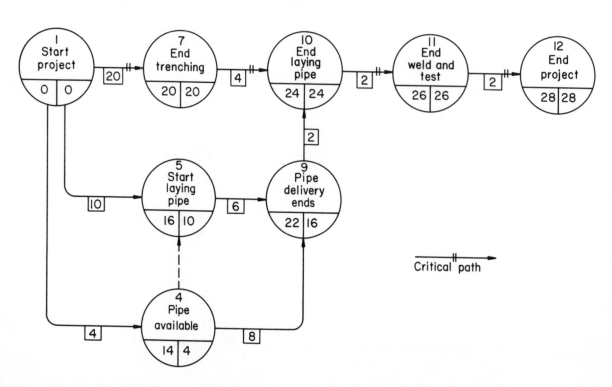

These conditions are used to determine the elapsed duration between milestones, to find the project duration, and to plot the critical path. The results are shown in Figure 4.

We started with the idea that an event-oriented network is an apparent aid for the observer, but we shall find shortly that it is of little *real* value for him.

Observer and Doer Requirements

For the *doer,* on the other hand, there is not even an apparent value to an event-oriented network created in the way that led to Figure 4. The doer is concerned with performing some operation or activity *which should be identified!* It does not help the doer to know that he is working between milestones; he doesn't need a diagram to know that a certain period of time will elapse between the start and finish of his work. But he does need a diagram that shows, at a glance and without any doubt whatsoever, what work must precede his, what is concurrent with his work, and what follows; he requires, that is, knowledge of the relationship of his activity, or work, to all other work in the project.

Is there some way to satisfy, with just one network, the requirements of both the observer and the doer? In order to find out, we must first list the requirements for each. The observer needs:

1. A rapid means of determining correct project status.

2. A means of correctly handling expected elapsed times to find the expected times for completion of each milestone.

3. A means of first finding the key milestones and then relating all of them into one project model.

4. A means of rapidly assimilating the scope of the whole project.

5. A means of determining the effects of various alternatives or corrective courses of action (if a revision is needed) before making a decision on what to do.

The doer needs:

1. A rapid means of determining the current status of his work in relation to the project as a whole.

2. A means of establishing resource needs and their necessary order of commitment so as to be able to schedule the use of available resources.

3. A means of rapidly assimilating the scope of the whole project.

4. A means of determining the effects of various alternatives or corrective courses of action (if a revision is needed) before deciding what to do.

As is evident from these lists, the needs of observer and doer are not widely different. In essence, both are following the action of the project, with the observer interested in *where* it is and the doer interested in *what* it is. A simple solution suggests itself for creating one diagram to meet the needs of both.

Activity Orientation with Labeled Milestones

Figure 5 shows an activity-oriented arrow diagram of the pipeline construction project. The junction points of arrows represent the completion of one or more actions, or operations, and we have called such junction points "events."

Now, consider the list of milestones used in creating the event-oriented network displayed in Figure 4. These same milestones are used to label various events of the activity-oriented arrow diagram for the pipeline project. The result, Figure 5, is a diagram that shows:

1. All the milestones.

2. The necessary work linkages between milestones. (These can be reduced to elapsed times related to actual work by adding up the duration of the necessary work. This is much more accurate than merely representing elapsed time between events by an arrow.)

3. A means of selecting other milestones that may have been omitted.

A study of Figure 5 shows that four events are not labeled as milestones; these are events 2, 3, 6, and 8. Event 3 is a junction point representing the fact that some trenching is done and that we could start laying pipe while we continue trenching. The actual start of the pipelaying function, however, requires both the availability of pipe *and* some completed trench. For that reason the dummy job (3,5) exists. If event 3 is to be a milestone, then it can best be labeled "(ready to start laying pipe)." On the other hand, events 2, 6, and 8 are, respectively, the points at which we actually start the trenching, weld and test, and backfilling operations. These events could, therefore, be labeled:

(Start trenching); event 2.
(Start weld and test); event 6.
(Start backfill); event 8.

The result is shown in Figure 6.

Let us take the estimated durations for the activities in the pipeline construction project (see Table 1) and apply them to the project diagram to find the project duration and the critical path. This result, also, is shown in Figure 6.

The project duration is given as 35 time units. But in Figure 4 *the duration for the same project is 28 time units! Furthermore, the critical path is different in each case.* Why? Which is correct?

FIGURE 5

Activity-oriented arrow diagram for pipelaying project with milestones labeled and all events numbered:

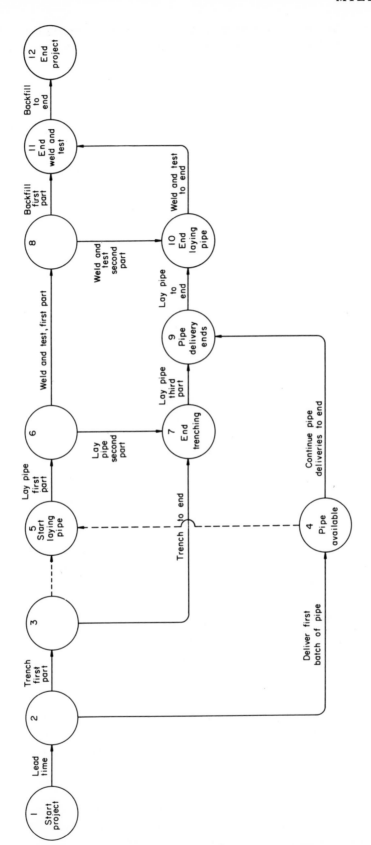

FIGURE 6

Project duration and critical path for activity-oriented arrow diagram with events labeled:

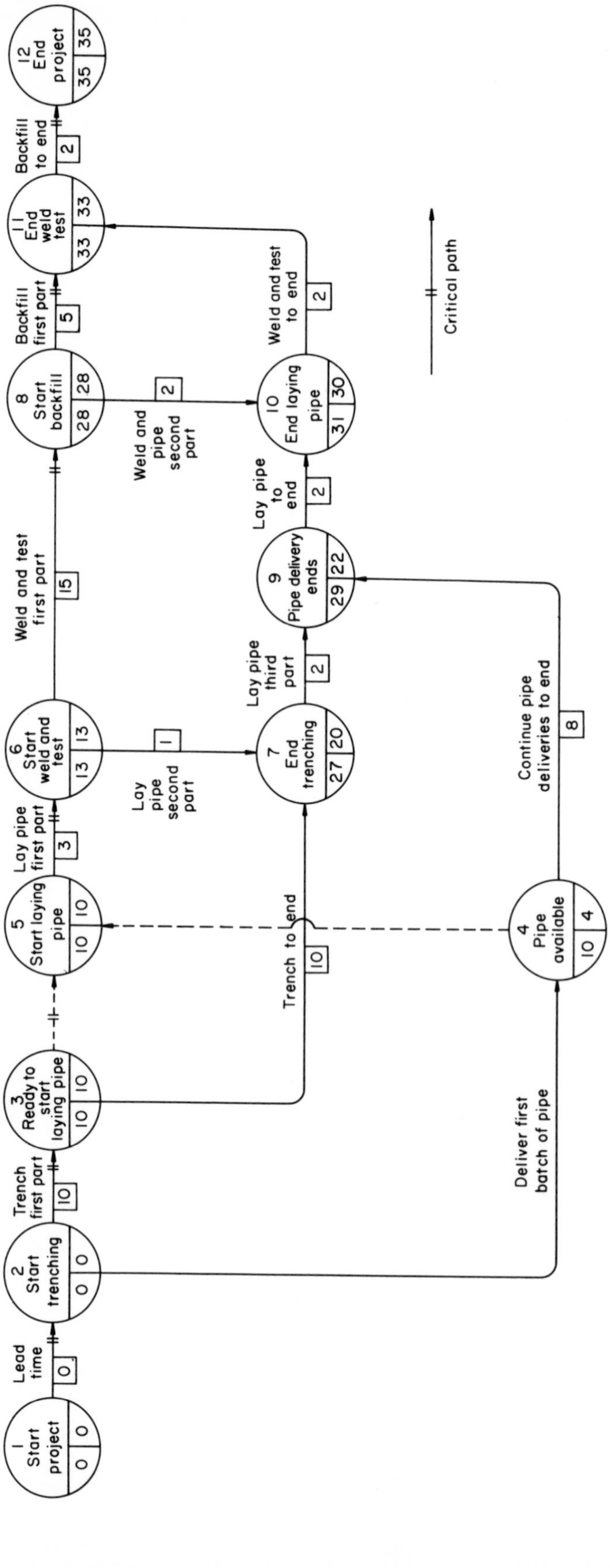

The arrow diagram (Figure 6) is correct, and the event-oriented diagram (Figure 4) is wrong. The reasons are quite obvious:

- Milestones are events in a project.

- Activities must be completed to reach a milestone since activities, or jobs, are the project elements.

- The time required to reach a milestone depends upon the work that must be done between milestones.

- We cannot estimate accurately the time between milestones without specifying the exact activities to take place.

- Hence, the estimated time to reach a milestone can only be accurately established by first estimating the actual work to be done.

- Hence, too, milestone charts produced with no relation to the actual work to be done are inadequate, and the results are quite probably inaccurate.

The reason for these errors is oversimplification, which has completely obscured the true relationships of the work to be done. Oversimplification is an opiate to be strongly avoided. Otherwise, errors will occur.

Let us see if the correct result for the project duration can be obtained from an event-oriented, or milestone, network if sufficient detail is included. To do so we select the 12 events as given in Figure 6 and use them as our milestones. This array of milestones is shown in Figure 7.

Detailed Event Networks

To complete the event-oriented network we must connect these events with arrows to represent elapsed time; in other words, we must link the milestones.

In order to simplify the description, these milestones have been prenumbered (ordinarily, they are numbered only after the network is completed) with the numbers used for these same events in Figure 6. Now let us establish the linkages as in Figure 8.

Events (1 and 2) must be connected since trenching is the first function. Event pairs—(2 and 7), (5 and 10), (4 and 9), (6 and 11), and (8 and 12)—must be connected since they represent the start and end of certain functions. Events (1 and 4) are connected to show an elapsed time from the start of the project to the availability of pipe. In this way, the two event pairs (5 and 6) and (6 and 8) are connected to show elapsed time between starting the three functions of pipelaying, weld and test, and backfill. Similarly, the three event pairs (7 and 10), (10 and 11), and (11 and 12) are connected for completion lags on the four functions of the pipeline project.

In addition, to keep the logic concerning the start of pipelaying correct, dummy linkages must be shown (no required time) between the two event

FIGURE 7

Milestone array for pipelaying project using same event numbers as shown in Figure 6

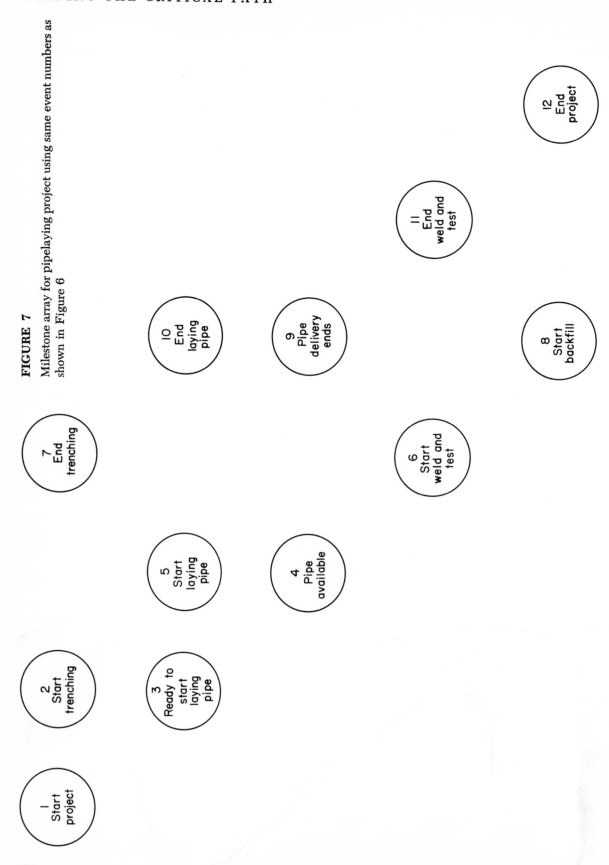

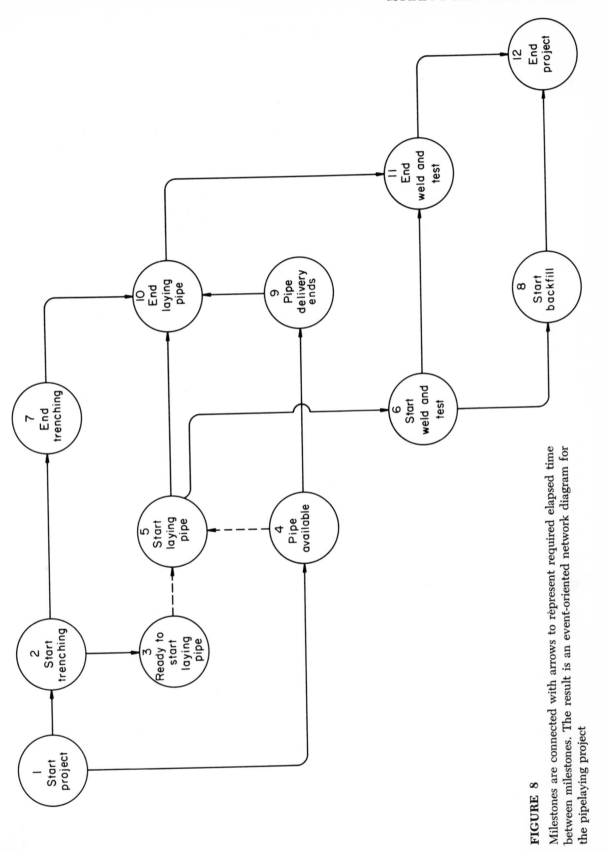

FIGURE 8

Milestones are connected with arrows to represent required elapsed time between milestones. The result is an event-oriented network diagram for the pipelaying project

pairs (3 and 5) and (4 and 5). The last linkage, between the pair (8 and 10), keeps the lag correct between the delivery of the last batch of pipe and the completion of pipelaying.

Figure 8 is, then, the event-oriented network equivalent to the arrow diagram of Figure 6. The duration values (Table 1) are used to find the project duration and the critical path. The result is shown in Figure 9.

We get the same project duration as we did with the activity-oriented diagram (Figure 6) and the same critical path, but the values for earliest and latest starting times at each event differ. Hence, even with more detail, we may get the right overall answer to satisfy an observer, but we cannot satisfy the doer, since we are not really certain about the *real* variation in starting time of non-critical jobs.

Summary

As a result of these considerations, it is clear that the only trustworthy and correct procedure to follow in creating an event-oriented network (if such a network is truly desired) is as follows:

1. Create an activity-oriented network.

2. Use the estimates of activity duration to find the values of E and L for each event in the diagram.

3. Select the milestone and label these events.

4. Produce a simplified network, if desired, showing only the selected milestones and their associated values of E and L as found in the activity-oriented diagram.

5. When there are changes, use the activity-oriented diagram to determine the revision or remedial action required if any. Change the activity-oriented diagram. Recalculate the critical path. Post the result to the milestone chart.

Proceeding in this way, we can meet the needs of *both the observer and the doer,* providing an event orientation for the observer and an activity orientation for the doer. However, as we shall see in the next volume, *Applied Operational Planning,* there is a better way to handle the needs of both simultaneously, using a single "time scale" (or project map) display.

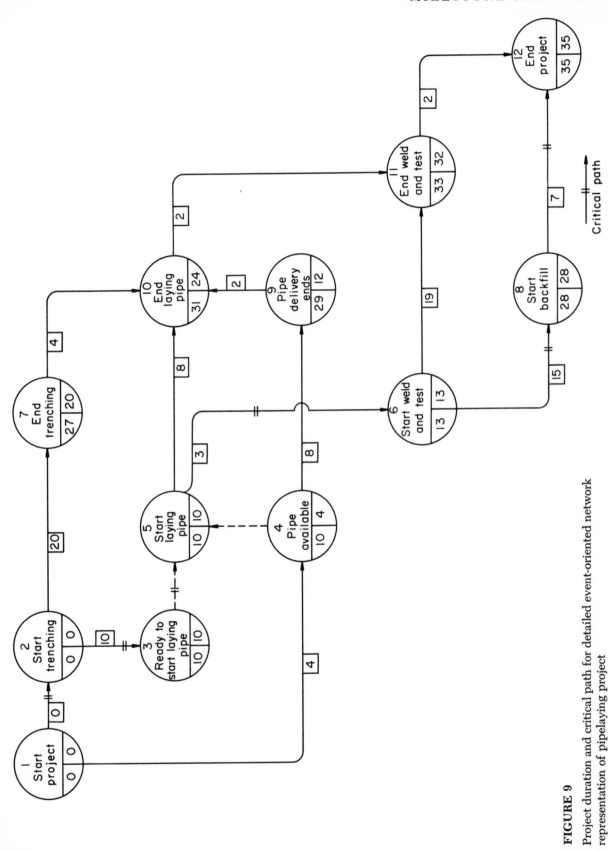

FIGURE 9

Project duration and critical path for detailed event-oriented network representation of pipelaying project

137

CHAPTER EIGHT

Finding the Critical Path: A Perspective

IN 1959 ONLY A HANDFUL of people had ever heard the term "critical path." Today, thousands of people are using PERT/CPM, in one way or another, to plan and schedule projects. In this intervening period PERT/CPM has been used for just about everything, including such projects as refinery turn-arounds, new refinery construction, plant expansions, preparation of budgets, and the selection of a company's new general manager.

The diagrams produced have had as many as 8,000 arrows and as few as 20 or 30; they have ranged in size from an 8½" x 11" page that fits into a standard notebook to a roll of paper 70' long and 48" wide especially mounted on a wooden roller so that it can be wound and unwound from either end.

The practitioners have ranged from draftsmen to corporate presidents, and arrow diagrams have been used in meetings of all kinds, including annual meetings of large corporations.

The results of applying these techniques have been almost unbelievable. In one refinery, the turn-around time was cut 25 per cent; in another, where the entire workforce had been on a three-shift basis for the whole turn-around, the critical path method study showed it was necessary to have less than half the total workforce on three shifts. In one design-and-build construction project, a total of five months was saved by eliminating bottle-necks in delivery of machines and design drawings. On a smaller scale, the maintenance time on a spindle unit in a chemical fiber plant was cut by almost 50 per cent after a PERT/CPM study.

And yet, with all the case histories to prove the tremendous power of PERT/CPM, and with all the users who point to its successful application, the truth of the matter is that *very few people really know* how to apply the method properly.

In order to explain this seeming paradox, it is first necessary to summarize what the critical path *really* is and how it should be used. The basic element is an arrow diagram representing a logical sequence of activities which must be performed in a project.

Once the diagram is completed, the next step is to introduce the element of time. By placing an estimated duration on each activity it is possible to calculate rapidly the longest path, *in terms of time*, through the network. This is called the critical path because the sum of durations equals the duration of the project. A delay in a critical job would delay the entire project by an equal amount, and a reduction of time in a critical job *may* reduce the duration of the project.

Project 502:

FIGURE 1

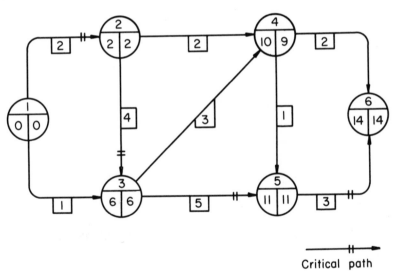

Critical path

In Figure 1 it can be seen that a delay in job (2,4) which produces a duration of six time units (say, days), instead of four, will delay the entire project by two days. On the other hand, if the duration of job (3,5) is cut to three days, or a reduction of two days on this one job only, the project will be shortened by one day because then the critical path will go through jobs (3,4) and (4,5) rather than through (3,5).

To most people, PERT/CPM is nothing more than an arrow diagram and a calculation of a critical path. In truth, this is only the start. *The critical path is not necessarily the most important thing.*

In order to understand this statement completely it should be remembered that the primary purpose of applying PERT/CPM to any project is to create

Finding the Plan and Schedule

a *plan* and a *schedule*. We define a "plan" as a coordinated model of the order in which we must perform all the activities required to complete our project. It is understood that the term "activities" includes not only the things we do (jobs) but also deliveries, inspections, and so on.

In the calculation procedures established for finding the critical path, two assumptions have been made: (1) that the duration of the activity is exactly known and (2) that the logic as shown in the arrow diagram is correct. We must, then, evaluate both of these assumptions and use the critical path itself to produce an optimum plan. Furthermore, we must evaluate the project duration as found by the critical path analysis in the light of a required completion date.

Once the plan is complete, scheduling can proceed. Scheduling is defined as the determination of the calendar date of resource use according to the total assigned resource capacity. This function can be properly performed only *after* the planning is complete. In order to produce a schedule, resource availability, job sequence, resource requirements, and possible job starting time (where such a range exists) must be taken into account.

While a knowledge of the critical path can be of assistance in producing a schedule, a knowledge of *only* the critical path makes it impossible to arrive at the ultimate schedule. PERT and CPM are *not* scheduling techniques. They establish the criteria for scheduling, but the technique intended for resource allocation and scheduling is MAP (Multiple Allocation Procedure). Once the schedule is produced, it can be displayed on a diagram or "map of the project" related to a time scale base.

In producing any schedule the requirement is to "level" resource use. This is accomplished by using total float to select the "best" job-starting time. The steps in developing the schedule are displayed in Figure 2.

FIGURE 2

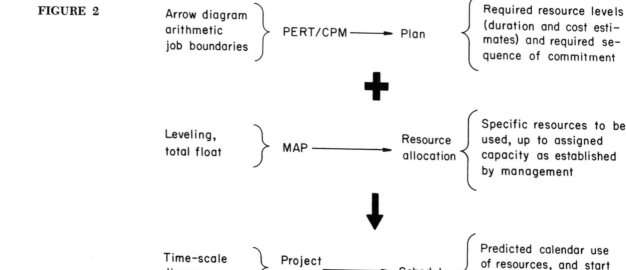

Arrow diagram arithmetic job boundaries } PERT/CPM ⟶ Plan { Required resource levels (duration and cost estimates) and required sequence of commitment

Leveling, total float } MAP ⟶ Resource allocation { Specific resources to be used, up to assigned capacity as established by management

Time-scale diagram } Project map ⟶ Schedule { Predicted calendar use of resources, and start and completion of each operation

140

The longest path in a project is determined not so much by the duration of the various jobs but by the number of men or machines which can be assigned out of the total resource capacity to complete each activity.

For example, it may be possible to paint a warehouse in five days with five men. It might also be possible to paint the warehouse in one day with 25 men, or in half a day with 50 men, or in an hour with 200 men. There is, however, an obvious fallacy. As jamming grows, efficiency drops off. While it may be just as efficient for five men to take five days as it is for ten men to take two and one-half days, it may require 50 men to do the job in one day instead of 25 men because of the drop in efficiency.

The requirement, therefore, is to establish a duration for the job with a varying crew size so that it is still within the limits of peak efficiency. This gives us a minimum cost for the job. We then take minimum duration, with a resultant maximum crew, and perform the critical path calculations with our estimate for job duration. This will give a minimum duration for the project, but it may very well result in personnel and equipment requirements which exceed our capabilities.

And there we have the heart of the *manpower allocation* problem. We have a plan which shows the proper sequence and the optimum crew size and minimum durations. In order to arrive at a schedule, which is our prime objective (so we can carry out the work required to complete our project), we must allocate our resource capacity according to the priority indicated by our plan.

While the distinction between planning and scheduling will be covered in depth in the next volume, a simple example can help illustrate this distinction now. Consider the project shown in Figure 1, in particular jobs (1,3), (2,3), (2,4), and (3,4). According to the plan (arrow diagram, critical path, and job boundaries), we have the data given below.

Job	Duration	Earliest		Latest		Total Float
		Start	Finish	Start	Finish	
(1,3)	1	0	1	5	6	5
(2,3)	4	2	6	2	6	0
(2,4)	2	2	4	8	10	6
(3,4)	3	6	9	7	10	1

In order to schedule all the jobs in the project, particularly these four, we must take into account resource needs *and* resource availability. Let us assume that the same man is required on all four jobs. In this case, while there are a number of possible schedules, the best one is:

Scheduled

Job	Start	Finish
(1,3)	1	2
(2,3)	2	6
(2,4)	6	8
(3,4)	8	11

As a result, the project cannot be completed until time 15, and a new critical path emerges. *After scheduling*, jobs (1,2), (1,3), (2,3), (2,4), (3,4), (4,5), and (5,6) are critical, and job (3,5) now has a total float of 1.

Planning and scheduling, in summary, are definitely *separate* functions.

The New, Total Approach

The new concept shown in Figure 3 represents the true approach—the *total* approach—to the application of PERT and CPM to determine a plan and schedule. The proper order is to plan and to allocate resources; the schedule is automatically determined. It is this failure to proceed beyond the determination of the critical path which has prevented most people from realizing the full benefits possible.

FIGURE 3

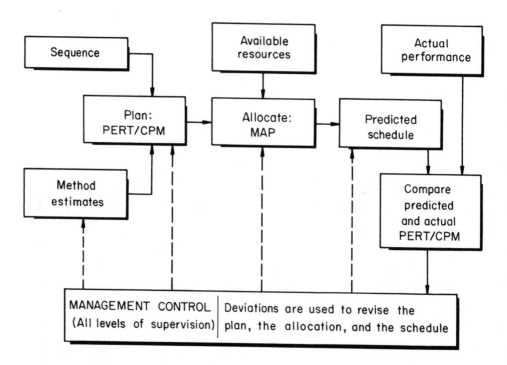

The *rules* for preparing an arrow diagram are simple, so simple as to be almost trivial. The *actual process* of preparation, on the other hand, is not simple and never trivial. Arrow diagrams are created, not by merely applying the rules, but rather by a searching analysis of the order in which activities must be performed, *not* the order in which things have been done in the past.

Becoming proficient in preparing arrow diagrams takes time and experience. It is more important to have at least three months, and preferably six months, of experience with such diagrams than to have an intimate knowledge of the project to be diagrammed. A man with this background in arrow diagramming is always better equipped than the man who knows the project.

As a matter of fact, complete knowledge of the project may be a liability. Often it results in a tendency to produce an arrow diagram in the order in which things have been done in the past, whereas the true requirement is to find the *best* sequence.

As shown in Figure 3, the preparation of the arrow diagrams is only the first step. Following this, estimates are made of time duration and crew sizes by those men who are closest to the work. The critical path is then calculated for the *normal* case and the resulting project duration is checked to see whether the estimates for individual jobs were realistic. In practice it has been found that estimates made by one man have a tendency to be all quite realistic, all low, or all high. By following through the entire logic it is possible to have a quick check on reliability. If everything checks out, the *optimum plan* is found, and then manpower allocation procedures are applied to implement the schedule.

Perhaps it may be best to end this volume with summarizing definitions of what we mean by project, planning, scheduling, and control. They follow.

Project Elements

Operations: the things which we or others do (activities or jobs) each with a sequential relation to all other operations; or an undertaking that uses resources for some period and involves duration and cost.

Resources: the things we use, normally reduced to a common standard of cost solely in terms of money. Actually, we spend in terms of men, machines, materials, money, and time.

Restraints, or conditions imposed by outside factors, such as completion dates, resource limits, deliveries (designs, materials, machines, manpower), approvals, inspections, and so on.

Planning Requirements

A master plan coordinating all project elements, that can serve as a working model for the project. The model must establish the required resources and their sequential order of commitment.

Scheduling Requirements

A calendar timetable establishing calendar dates of resource use according to requirement. Scheduled resource use must never be greater than resources actually available and actual use must be leveled over the project period.

Control Requirements

A dynamic response to permit management by exception.

Finding the Critical Path and Project Management

In Volume 2, *Applied Operational Planning*, we shall be concerned with using the critical path itself to produce an optimum plan and with the inclusion of required or imposed completion dates which may differ from the project duration found from the basic critical path analysis.

Applied Operational Planning is further concerned with scheduling criteria, activity and project costs, and control for *all* levels of management. The concepts of MAP and PERT/COST are introduced there, too.

The objective in applying PERT/CPM to a project is to produce a plan and schedule and provide control during the project implementation; that is, to serve as a tool in the function of project management. Finding the critical path is the first step, and a vital one, in using PERT/CPM in the management of a project.